First Woman Ambulance Surgeon

Emily Barringer

BORN: September 27, 1876

DIED: April 9, 1961

On a winter day in 1902 the newspapers in New York City printed a story that provoked a storm of controversy—for the first time in the history of the United States a woman was allowed to intern in a hospital. For Emily Barringer, a slender, attractive woman in her mid-twenties, the appointment was the climax of eight years of diligent study and sacrifice. From the first day the doctors who were her superiors subjected her to severe persecution, but she always proved more than equal to the tasks given her. She became a doctor, beloved by patients and nurses, respected by her colleagues, and at twenty-eight she was officially appointed House Surgeon in charge of Gouverneur Hospital.

Books by Iris Noble

Biographies

CLARENCE DARROW

THE COURAGE OF DR. LISTER

THE DOCTOR WHO DARED
William Osler

GREAT LADY OF THE THEATRE
Sarah Bernhardt

JOSEPH PULITZER
Front Page Pioneer

NELLIE BLY
First Woman Reporter

WILLIAM SHAKESPEARE

FIRST WOMAN AMBULANCE SURGEON
Emily Barringer

EGYPT'S QUEEN: CLEOPATRA

EMPRESS OF ALL RUSSIA:
Catherine the Great

Novels

ONE GOLDEN SUMMER

STRANGER NO MORE

THE TENDER PROMISE

First Woman Ambulance Surgeon

Emily Barringer

by IRIS NOBLE

Julian Messner   New York

Published by Julian Messner
Division of Pocket Books, Inc.
8 West 40 Street, New York 10018

Fourth Printing, 1966

Printed in the United States of America

Library of Congress Catalog Card No. 62–10194

From kindness and generosity, Dr. Emily Dunning Barringer used fictitious names for the four doctors who were senior to her at Gouverneur Hospital and who endeavored to make her resign her position there, when she wrote the story of her experiences, *Bowery to Bellevue*. The author of this book could do no less than follow her lead in concealing the true identities.

First Woman
Ambulance
Surgeon
Emily Barringer

1

Eight-year-old Emily crouched on the broad stairway just below the second floor landing. From there she could peer over that top step and look down the hallway to Mama's bedroom. As the door opened or closed, as the nurse darted in and out, there was a thin, wavering streak of lamplight which lighted up the hall carpet or filtered into dim shadows as the door half closed again. Sounds came from behind it—a stifled cry, now and then, from Mama, or the rustle of the nurse's skirts, or a few soft words in Lil's Irish brogue.

Most important of all, it seemed to Emily, was the deeper, heavier voice of Dr. Burchard. When *he* spoke, things happened. The nurse would say "Yes, Doctor" or Lil would come flying out and run downstairs to the kitchen for kettles of hot water.

What was happening? It was all very strange. It was frightening, because Mama was sick. That much Emily knew.

Lil was their old nursemaid, yet she had seen Emily on the steps and said nothing about bedtime. No one had paid any attention to the younger children either, and for the first time in her small life Emily had done a grownup's job. An hour ago she had seen to it that Margaret and Amy and Harry had brushed their teeth and said their prayers and were safe in bed. She had looked for Will, her older brother, but couldn't find him; she was lonely and frightened and couldn't sleep—and the stairway was as close as she dared come to Mama.

An instinct told her that she would not be allowed in Mama's bedroom, but an even stronger instinct kept her where she was, within sight and hearing.

The doorbell sounded down below. Emily waited a second for a maid to answer it before she remembered that there were no maids or butler any more, only Lil upstairs and Cook down in the kitchen. Lil came hurrying past her, went down and opened the door to admit another man in a dark frock coat and a big, soft leather bag.

"I'm Dr. William Lusk," she heard him say. "Dr. Burchard is expecting me. I understand it's a difficult birth and he thinks I may have to operate." He was following Lil up the steps as he spoke and Lil was answering: "Yes, Doctor, yes. Ah, the poor darling—my poor, beautiful mistress."

He went into the bedroom, too, and now the door was closed tightly and there was no lamplight at all in the hallway. Still Emily stayed where she was. Perhaps she dozed a little because she was suddenly startled to find Lil bending over her, shaking her and saying:

"Emily! Child, would you be after helping me this once?" Her voice held its usual kindness but she wasn't smiling. "I do need you. I can't be leaving them upstairs, with the doctors wanting something from me every blessed minute. And it's fearful I am of leaving your mother. She's quieter, someways, when I'm in the room."

"What do you want me to do?" asked Emily. "Let me do something."

The middle-aged woman, who had been nursemaid as long as Emily could remember, handed her the slip of paper. "I want you to go down the street to Haas's pharmacy and ask them to give you these medicines written on the piece of paper. Do hurry, there's a dear child. The doctors are wanting these special like." She stooped and kissed the soft, babyish cheek and walked away with quick steps to Mama's bedroom.

"But—Lil—" Emily was so astounded she could not believe

it. She had always been a very protected and sheltered little girl. She never was allowed to go anywhere on her own.

"Hurry, child!" the nursemaid called over her shoulder.

Emily walked down the steps, half expecting at any moment that Lil would call her back and say it was a mistake. Go out into the street at night alone? Had Lil forgotten how often she had said Emily was never, never to go out at night by herself? There were bad men out there. One of the maids had once scared the children with goblins and witches that roamed the streets at night.

Hurry, Lil had said. The doctor wanted these medicines. Emily got her coat out of the hall closet, fluffed her long blond hair so that it spread like a fan over her brown velvet coat collar, pulled on her mittens and managed, by using both hands, to open the heavy lock of the front door.

She had got this far but the minute she stared out into the dark street her courage failed. There was a dim gas lamp on a tall standard halfway down the block but that was all. The rest was dark. She knew where Haas's pharmacy was but she couldn't see the store lights from where she was.

She almost went back. Then she thought of those two men in their dark coats, those two doctors who were doing their best to make Mama well again. They were depending on her now and she had to go on.

One step, then another and another. A cat slunk by, his eyes gleaming with witch fire, green-gold in the dark. Emily shivered. She passed a house and felt better because she knew the people who lived there. If anything happened she could run up and pound on their door. Another step—she must walk faster. *Hurry*, Lil had said.

"One, two, button my shoe—three, four, shut the door—" she made herself say the nursery rhyme very fast so that she would walk fast. She talked to herself: I am Emily Dunning. I live at one East Eighteenth Street in New York City. I have two brothers and two sisters. This is 1884 and I was born in 1876. I am—

There were footsteps behind her. And on her right there loomed up the big, dark gaping hole which was the mouth of an alleyway. Panic stricken, she broke and ran as fast as she could, her head down so that she didn't see the curb when she had to cross the street and she stumbled; she didn't see the horse and cart and ran in front of them.

But after she crossed that street she could see red-and-green-lights and she knew they were in the pharmacy window. On and on she ran and finished up, breathless, pushing open the door and jumping inside. She was panting and shaken.

"Why, it's little Emily Dunning," said the kind voice. Mr. Haas looked at her over his spectacles and came around from behind his counter. "What are you doing out alone, at this hour of night?"

She handed him the paper. "No one else could come, Mr. Haas, because Mama is sick and Lil is helping the doctor and she said to please hurry and bring back these things."

"Now, you are a brave girl, indeed." He took the list and moved quickly to his shelves, pulling down bottles and boxes and measuring out mysterious powders into other small boxes. "A very brave little girl."

"Am I? Really?" Somehow, being frightened wasn't terrible at all, when you were told you were brave, instead.

He nodded. "Just like your mother. Mrs. Dunning is one of the bravest women I know. Just like you, when something has to be done she does it, even if she thinks she can't. Bravery doesn't always show on the outside. Why, as long as I've known your mother—and your grandfather gave her that beautiful house when your brother Will was born—all that time I would have said she was just a fairy princess, so lovely in her velvets and furs and jewels and her carriages and all. . . ."

As he talked, he worked fast, measuring liquid into a bottle and then grinding up powders with pestle and mortar. "Now, suddenly, your family's lost all its money, just as so many others have. Economic crisis, it's called. I wouldn't have thought your mother could have stood up to such a trial, but the last time she was in here Mrs. Dunning was smiling just as she always does and she said, 'We'll manage, Mr. Haas. We'll manage, somehow.' "

Emily didn't understand. It had something to do with Papa going away to France, "on business," and not having any maids in the house. But it was nice of Mr. Haas to talk to her as if she weren't just eight years old. "I think," she said solemnly, "that I am growing up, Mr. Haas."

He placed the medicines in her hands very carefully. His eyes twinkled and he said, "Yes, Emily, I think you are."

It was comforting to know that he stood in the doorway and watched her all the way to her house, but she was only a bit scared this time. She ran because Lil was waiting for her.

Emily hardly slept at all that night. Once the door of Mama's bedroom was closed tight for a long time, with both doctors and the nurse and Lil in there, so Emily wandered back to the nursery rooms. She found Amy and Harry asleep and all right, but Margaret was uncovered. She pulled the blanket up and tucked it in.

Will had his own room, now that he was almost ten, but his door was open and he called to her: "Emily?" He sat up in bed when she came in. "How is Mama?"

"I don't know." She sat on his bed and they talked. "I helped the doctor, Spreckles. I went to Mr. Haas's pharmacy for medicine. All by myself."

Will wasn't impressed. He nodded his head. "That's good. We have to help Mama a lot from now on, you and I. I've been helping carry up the coals for the fireplaces and locking the windows at night—and tomorrow I'm going to rake the leaves on the back lawn, under the tree."

She looked at him, amazed. Will had been doing all these things and she had never noticed. Now that she did think of it, who else would have seen that the fires were lit and who else would do all the jobs that the butler and the man of all work used to do? She sighed.

"I wish you would tell me. Why must we help now?"

"Lil told me," he explained. "We haven't any money any more. We used to be rich but we aren't now. So we mustn't ask for bicycles or new dresses or toys, and we can't go to Rowsley this summer because it has been sold."

"*Rowsley?*" She had been born on September 27, 1876, in that great, splendid house called Rowsley, in Scarsdale, and she loved it even more than this home in New York. Rowsley was paradise, with its rolling, spreading, velvety lawns and all the trees to climb, the gardens, the peacocks and the house itself—so many, many elegant rooms.

Will did his best to make her understand that their fortune was gone; that Rowsley had had to be sold; that their father had had to go to France and stay there so that he could try to build up their finances once more. In the meantime, Mama owned this house and that was all. Their various uncles and aunts had offered to take one or more of the children but Mama was determined they would all stay together. She was going to take in "paying guests"; luckily, this house in New York was so big that there were lots of extra bedrooms.

"So you see, Emily, why we have to help?" Will thumped his pillow. "Even if you are a girl, there is a lot you can do."

"I don't see what difference it makes if I am a girl. Girls can do as much as boys, can't they?" she looked at him in surprise and he was instantly ashamed.

"You're right. I'm sorry, honest. I just said that because that's the way grown-up men always talk. We'll make a promise—in this family we'll all work together, boys and girls." He yawned. "I'm sleepy. I wish Lil would come and tell us Mama is all right." His eyes closed even before he finished speaking.

Emily slipped away to keep her all-night vigil on the stairway. Sometimes she dozed; sometimes she was half awake and half asleep. During those times she would wait until she heard the doctors' voices or caught a glimpse of them; comforted by their presence she would doze off again.

Toward morning Lil found her there and carried her off to bed and whispered to her, while she was being undressed. "You have a new baby brother and—praise be!—Mrs. Dunning is safe and well."

The next day when Emily woke up she found it was true— she had a baby brother. Mama was very weak and there was plenty of work for even an eight-year-old girl. She dressed quickly, helped the younger children with buttons that were hard to reach and took them down to the dining room where Cook had already set out milk and porridge. As quickly as she could, she ran upstairs to help Lil.

Lil, too, seemed to know that a big change had come about and that Emily was no longer a child. All day long it was: "Emily, will you run down and ask Cook for some broth for your mother?" or "Emily, will you stand here and watch your baby brother?" or "Emily, will you run, child, and see what the children are doing? Don't let them climb too high in the pear tree."

The next day Mrs. Dunning was considerably better and Emily was allowed in to see her, and in the bedroom she could actually help the nurse. It was wonderful to see Mama's faint but proud smile as the little girl fetched glasses of water, held the tray when the nurse measured out the drops of medicine, and fetched and carried whatever doctor and nurse wanted.

Before the month was out Mrs. Dunning was up and fast regaining her usual energy. Just as Emily herself had changed, she saw the change in her mother. No longer was she the elegant Mrs. Dunning who used to confer in French with her French chef over what to serve for one of her famous dinner parties—there was no longer a chef and no more parties. No longer did she spend hours with her favorite seamstress over the latest fashions and the imported satin brocade for her dresses—there was no longer any money for seamstresses or for new dresses.

It was as if Mama had taken a deep breath, closed a door on her old life and immediately started a new one. She, who had never cooked, learned how to make delicious meals out of the cheapest cuts of meat and the cheapest vegetables. Her slim, delicate hands had done exquisite needlework and embroidery; now she hemmed towels and made shirts for the boys. She scrubbed. She cleaned. Always before, she had bought things without any thought of price; now she saved, budgeted and scrimped.

Mrs. Dunning had no trouble attracting paying guests. Her house was noted for its elegance and charm. One part of the house she reserved for her own family. The rest, with the best bedrooms and sitting rooms, was for the guests. The beautiful gray parlor, where the imported wallpaper and the velvet carpet were a soft dove-gray, where the gold-framed mirrors reflected the white-and-gold painted woodwork and the crystal chandelier, was shared by both family and guests.

Mrs. Dunning had been a superb hostess and she still was. No matter how hard she worked during the day, she presided with grace and charm at night. In the gray parlor she served her guests, seated behind the massive silver coffee service, and Emily, as she handed around the coffee cups, copied her mother and learned the manners of a lady.

The children found it was fun to have guests in the house. Even famous people came; Rudyard Kipling, the author, was a frequent visitor since his sister and niece lived in two of Mrs. Dunning's bedrooms.

Some of the guests became, truly, part of the family. When Dr. Burchard's wife died, he brought his two boys to Mrs. Dunning and she took them in. Now there were eight children, instead of six, and Emily and Will had their hands full after school, managing them all.

Their father's business kept him more and more in Europe, as he tried, with but small success, to build back their fortunes. He was a beloved visitor to the children, but he could come to America so rarely that they could love him only as a stranger. It was their mother who was the center of their lives, the one who made all the decisions for them.

It was she who decided that the special French tutor must go and that they must give up the dancing lessons, but that somehow the money must be found to keep them in the best private academic schools in New York. For Emily and her sisters, this meant Miss Brackett's. It was a lucky choice. Miss Brackett was a nineteenth century pioneer; she made her girls work hard at Latin, mathematics and science, instead of stressing the usual deportment and singing lessons.

The minute school was over, Emily hurried home to help her mother. Baby Ned was her special charge and she became as skillful as her mother in taking care of him.

As the children all grew older, each one learned to help. The promise that Emily and Will had made to each other was kept: there was a true democracy in the Dunning family and boys and girls worked together, played together, argued and settled their differences together, without any idea that a boy might be superior to a girl.

It was not until they were in their teens that Emily learned, with a rude shock, that the outside world did not agree with this idea.

When he was sixteen Will left school and got a job as an office boy. It was a proud moment when he brought home his first week's salary—three dollars—and put it in his mother's hands. Emily was thrilled and envious. If Will could do it, why couldn't she? Next year she would be fifteen and she, too, would bring home a pay check.

But in 1890 the world thought differently.

"Girls can't do this," her mother explained gently. "It is thought quite proper and manly for a boy to go to work. Will's employers will help him; he'll have chances to get ahead in business, or if he should want to go on to college later on, it's possible for a boy to work and go to school, too. A girl's place is in the home until she is married. If we were destitute, you might have to work in a factory or a shop, but that wouldn't be the same as Will's job. It would be sheer drudgery without a chance to get ahead."

"What can girls do?" demanded Emily, not entirely satisfied.

Mrs. Dunning's courageous heart almost failed her. She looked at her extremely pretty young daughter—a slim, blue-eyed, blonde, with a gracefully shaped face and clear, soft, petal-smooth complexion—and the right answer to Emily's question rose to her lips but could not be said.

Marriage was the one and only thing for a girl in those days. But where could a husband be found for Emily? In spite of the fact that the Dunnings were now poor, all of their friends, all of the people they knew, all of Emily's classmates at Miss Brackett's, were well to do and many were rich. All took it for granted that wealth went with their social position. Mrs. Dunning knew that world; it had been hers. She knew that no mother of an eligible young man would want the penniless Emily as a daughter-in-law.

Emily was still too young, but the marriage game was already beginning. In their circle, parties and dances were already being arranged so that the "right" young boys could meet the "right" young girls and the foundations laid for the courtships to come.

The Dunnings could neither afford to give such parties nor to go to them. Up to now there had been no distinctions because of money; as children, Emily and her sisters had gone to dances and parties at the homes of their classmates, and their friends had loved the informal fun at the Dunnings, particularly the romps at Christmas and after Christmas, on Twelfth-Night, when the tree was taken down and all the children piled onto it to slide it down the basement stairs.

It was different now—for Emily. And it would be so for Margaret in a few years. Margaret was dark while Emily was fair, yet both were pretty. What good would that prettiness do them?

Mrs. Dunning thought with some bitterness and perplexity, what good would it do that Emily was unusually intelligent? That she was Miss Brackett's brightest pupil? That she had such a special talent with her hands in a sickroom, the tender ability to manage a crying child, a wisdom beyond her years?

It was expecting too much to think that some young man would see beyond Emily's poverty to Emily's richness of personality and talents.

"Don't worry, Mama," the girl insisted, when she saw that her mother was troubled. "Let Will go out and work. You need me here at home to help take care of the family."

She could say that at fourteen, but in September 1894, when she would be eighteen and starting her last year at Miss Brackett's—what after that? Not only were Margaret and Amy able to take care of themselves, but Margaret had proved to be an exceptional student, completely in command of herself. Amy had even earned money tutoring another girl. Harry was working in a dentist's office. Ned was a self-sufficient ten-year-old, fully capable of taking care of himself. There was plenty of work in the house but Mama had everything running fairly smoothly.

The problem of what to do about Emily was becoming acute. No fairy prince had appeared, breaking Society's rules to court the poor but beautiful girl; she was no longer needed so desperately at home. On the other hand, she was no mouse, and with her brains and fiery spirit and courage she was bound, sooner or later, to break loose from the home ties.

Mrs. Dunning worried a great deal about that. She had been brought up to believe that a woman's place was in the home and that everything outside of it was a man's world. She did not at all approve of these modern women who were calling for votes for women and equal rights for women and careers for women. "There are two things," she told her girls, "that I never want a daughter of mine to do—smoke a cigarette or march in a woman suffrage parade."

Emily had no desire to smoke but she was fascinated by the suffrage parades down Fifth Avenue and what they stood for. She thought these modern women were valiant, carrying banners in their parades and suffering boos and taunts and even stones being hurled at them. So when she heard that Dr. Anna Putnam Jacobi was to speak on "Education for Women" she begged to be permitted to attend the meeting.

"I can and must work, Mama," she said, setting her soft chin into a new, determined firmness. "Teaching and nursing —I suppose it will have to be one of those, since they are the only things I can do and still be a lady. But I haven't the slightest notion how one becomes a nurse and it is quite possible that Dr. Jacobi might speak about that tonight."

Reluctantly, Mrs. Dunning agreed. She was by no means reconciled to Emily's having a career; the idea was shocking. For reasons that were mixed up in her own mind, she went to the meeting, chaperoning Emily and Margaret. Dr. Jacobi's daughter was a good friend of Margaret's since they were both in the same class at Miss Brackett's, and the Dunning girls had been invited to many lovely dances at the Jacobi home. Reasoning thus, it was only polite to accept the invitation to the lecture. However, without saying so to the girls, Mrs. Dunning was as curious about that woman Dr. Jacobi as

Emily was. To both of them she was a creature from a different world.

Anna Putnam was certainly a gentlewoman, the daughter of the Putnam publishing family. Anna Putnam Jacobi, wife of one of New York's most eminent doctors, was happily married, a wonderful mother to her children, a doctor in her own right and one of the best. She had fought every inch of the way and had gone as far in her profession as anyone could in America.

As a young woman she had been graduated as a chemist and pharmacist from the Female Medical College of Pennsylvania. This was not enough. She wanted a medical degree. She could work as hard as any man and she couldn't see why she shouldn't attend a medical college for men, where the standards were much higher than those of any woman's college. This was impossible in America and so she went to France to study.

She attended the University of Paris, where she was told she would get no credit for her courses. Never mind, she told herself. Credit or not, she was going to become a doctor. The professors were so struck by her persistence that they gave her not only her credits but a degree as well. This was in 1871.

When she returned to the United States there was, naturally, no place for her at any "regular" hospital. The big hospitals accepted only male doctors. So she became a member of the Women's Medical College faculty in New York and set herself up in private practice.

The Women's Medical College was associated with the New York Infirmary for Women and Children, founded by the famous Blackwell sisters, Elizabeth and Emily. It was a college hospital run by women for women and children patients. Yet the fame of Dr. Anna Putnam Jacobi reached out far beyond it.

This was the woman whom Emily so much wanted to see

and hear. Excited, curious, thrilled with her own daring, feeling somehow that life itself was pushing her forward, Emily walked down the aisle of the lecture hall behind her mother and sister and they found seats near the front.

None of their own friends was there. The audience was a strange one to them: women, almost mannish, in severely tailored dresses; a few in fur coats or fashionable broadcloth, but for the most part there were shabbily dressed, poorer women, but with faces and eyes that were challenging in their fire and sincerity.

Then Anna Putnam Jacobi appeared on the small platform.

She was short, thick set and dark, but the force of her magnetic personality overrode her appearance. She was someone to command respect.

"Education," she began, without preliminaries, "is the one certain way of raising the position of women from that which it is now—dependency upon men, submission to men—in many cases, chattel slavery to men. A woman cannot demand rights if she is not qualified for them. She cannot vote if she does not understand politics. She cannot teach unless she has been taught. She cannot become a lawyer, a businesswoman, a doctor, unless she has had the training to fit her for those positions."

Her audience was quiet, listening. "We have all heard it said," she went on, "that education—too much of it—makes a woman unfit to be a good wife or mother. She loses her femininity. I am not the only woman who has proved by example that this just is not true."

Someone broke into applause but Dr. Jacobi raised her hand to check it. She had too much to say for interruptions. "The theory that men will always protect and support the woman might be fine, in theory, but how often does it work out in practice? Men cannot always guarantee security to their families, no matter how much they try, and so wives—untrained, unskilled—must go to work at whatever they can, to help support the family."

Emily felt her mother stir beside her. That shot had gone home.

"And what of unmarried women?" Dr. Jacobi's voice went ringing through the hall. "Haven't they suffered enough degradation? Is a woman any less a person, any less talented or intelligent or charming, simply because she doesn't marry? You know as well as I do the fate of the unmarried. As a spinster daughter or sister-in-law, she is tolerated in someone else's home to be everyone's drudge. Or she has to take in sewing, millinery or work in a shop. The wages are miserable and she is looked down upon by everyone."

For the rest of the lecture Emily was in a daze. Dr. Jacobi spoke of women's colleges and their struggles to raise their standards, and of those very, very few men's colleges where a few women students were permitted attendance. To Emily, who loved school and learning, it was as if the lecturer were describing a paradise.

When the lecture was over, she tried to tell her mother how she felt but Mrs. Dunning wouldn't listen. "Not tonight, please. We'll discuss this some other time," was all she would say. Her daughters both understood; their mother had found the lecture to be too much for her. It was too new, too revolutionary, too unconventional, and it had confused her more than it had helped.

The next day after school, Emily hurried home, anxious to talk of her future. It was no use. She and her mother sat sewing, with the windows open for the first gentle warmth of spring, and Mrs. Dunning wanted to talk only of her own girlhood, her courtship and marriage.

Emily understood. Her heart ached for her mother, and just a little for herself. Mrs. Dunning was really speaking of what she wanted for her daughters; she had been a belle in Boston, surrounded by wealthy suitors, petted and spoiled and adored by all. How could Emily tell her that she didn't care for such things? That a brilliant debut and the attentions of men were nothing, compared to the kind of future Dr. Jacobi had spoken about?

She tried once, gently. "I'll get married, Mama—sometime. We don't have to think of that yet. I should like to do something on my own first."

"Oh, Emily, you want to be a nurse but you have no idea how hard that life is! It's not what I wanted for you and—"

The doorbell rang, cutting off her words. The maid ushered in a visitor, a lady who was a dear friend of Mrs. Dunning's, and the two older women settled themselves for a chat in the parlor. Since the visitor was not a particular favorite of Emily's—in spite of her genuine kindness, she had the settled assurance and slight arrogance of the securely rich—the girl exchanged only a few polite words, made her curtsy and then returned to her sewing.

She was in the room next to the parlor, with the door wide open. She could see them and occasionally even hear their conversation, but she worked on, undisturbed, trimming new bonnets with gay ribbons. Easter was coming.

For a while her own thoughts were on the lecture of the night before, then, suddenly, she caught what the visitor was saying and she knew they were speaking of her.

". . . a lovely, lovely girl, Fanny." The words were addressed to her mother, yet Emily could feel the lady's eyes resting on her. "Such a pity that her looks will not help her. One has to be practical about such things. I mean no offense, but you know as well as I do that she has no dowry. Young men would be afraid they would not only have to support her but help her younger sisters as well."

Color was burning in Mrs. Dunning's cheeks. She was proud. Only because of their long friendship would she have permitted the visitor to speak so frankly. She tried to turn the conversation but the lady would not be diverted.

"No," she continued, "Emily must think, instead, of help-ing you. She must make herself useful; certainly, you do need the money, though you have done wonders until now. The younger children are growing and the older they get, the more they will need. Emily must earn her living. She's clever enough," she added, glancing at the girl's fingers as they expertly stitched on the ribbons. "Why not have her appren-ticed to a milliner? I'm sure she could make a success of it. I will be glad to speak to my milliner about her."

She rose. Mrs. Dunning accompanied her to the door, let her out and then called sharply, "Emily—come here, im-mediately."

At that strange tone, that peremptory summons so unlike her mother, the sewing scattered off the girl's lap and she ran into the parlor. Her mother was standing tall, tense and de-fiant against the door, her hands flat at her sides, pressing hard into the very wood. There was agony, humiliation and pain in her eyes—but there was also anger and resolve in the set of her mouth.

"Emily, you heard the conversation just now?"

The girl nodded. One blond braid slipped out of its coil from the top of her head, making her look even younger and more vulnerable in her mother's eyes.

"Well, that settles the question." Mrs. Dunning's voice was the strangest Emily had ever heard. "*You* are going to college."

"Mama!" Emily sat down, suddenly. She was shaking so that she couldn't stand. "Do you really mean it? I am not to be apprenticed to a milliner?"

The pain was fading from her mother's eyes but the resolve was, if anything, strengthening. "Never. You, with your fine and brilliant mind, to be forced to sit ten hours a day in some dark corner of a milliner's back room, bending over stitches, at the beck and call of an employer who will work you until you are exhausted—having to say 'yes, ma'am' and 'no, ma'am' to some impudent, fashionable customer? I've seen these poor apprentices. Their lives are nothing but slavery. Perhaps someday there will be laws passed to protect them, but now there are none. No, you are going to college," she repeated stubbornly.

How dare anyone say that the future of her daughters was hopeless! How dare anyone say that they were doomed to semislavery and that she, their mother, could do nothing for them!

2

Emily found, once her mother had made up her mind, that while there might be mountains of problems, there was not the slightest speck of doubt about it—she was going to college.

The first thing was to call a family conference. All the Dunnings were informed of the news and they all reacted as if the great adventure were to be as much theirs as Emily's. They were astounded and delighted.

An ordinary family, without their special working-together, all-for-one closeness, might well have objected. As it was, there was little enough money for a new dress or a hat or shoes, and seldom enough for a treat. Now there would be even less money for them—and they behaved as if Emily were doing them a favor!

"We won't spend one cent on summer vacations this year. We'll save it for Emily's tuition." This was from Amy.

"Amisha—" Emily protested, but Margaret interrupted.

"I'll make your clothes," she said. "You sew well, but I have a better sense of style than you do." And she did. With a scrap of lace, a bit of ribbon or a new, starched collar, Margaret always managed to look as if she just stepped out of the latest bandbox fashion.

"I'm earning more now. We'll put that extra dollar away every single week and by the end of the year that will be fifty-two dollars toward the tuition." Will had earned that extra dollar raise in a way that was typical of him. Though he was just an office boy, with no responsibility, he had noticed one day that his boss had left the safe open at the lunch hour. Will ran through the streets, found his employer in his favorite restaurant and warned him about the open safe. His boss was so grateful that Will's salary had been raised, on the spot.

"If you'll pack a bigger lunch for me," Harry contributed, "and put in two apples instead of one, I won't be tempted to buy a bun in the middle of the afternoon. Apples are better for me, anyway." He grinned at Emily.

Tears of gratitude and joy misted her eyes. Though she loved her family dearly, it was Harry—whose name was actually Henry and whom they all called "Pads" for a reason they had long forgotten—who somehow knit them together. He had a sense of humor and he teased them all unmercifully, sharply stinging them for any false pride or selfishness, yet of them all, he was the one who dared to be openly, frankly sentimental. Whatever Pads felt, he showed and he was showing now, by the great happiness in his face, how willingly he would give up his own small pleasure for her.

"Pads—all of you—it doesn't seem right that you should have to give up so much for me. I promise," Emily said fervently, "that I will finish as quickly as possible so I can earn money and you can go to college, too."

Mrs. Dunning objected. "You are not to feel in debt to us, Emily. If you feel that way, you'll be tempted to cut short your studies and take the first position offered. No, we want you to get the most out of this opportunity." Between Dr. Jacobi's lecture, which had shown her a new dignity for women, and the choice offered by her friend, that of enslaving Emily in a millinery apprenticeship, Mrs. Dunning was in revolt against everything she had formerly believed. "If you succeed, somehow we'll find the money to send Amy and Margaret to college, too, if they want it. I'm not worried about the boys. Boys have much better chances to make their own way in this world."

Emily had more than a year to go before she would finish at Miss Brackett's, but they had to plan for the money now. They talked of possibly taking in more boarders or selling what was left of Mrs. Dunning's jewels, the family silver or the better pieces of porcelain. Though they came to no final decision, they were agreed that somehow the money would be found.

And before the council broke up, their mother astonished them again by saying that she had written to Dr. Jacobi for an interview and advice. Then Harry stood up. They had all been drinking hot chocolate as they talked; now he raised his cup solemnly and said, "To the family!"

They all drank the toast. It was a historic moment for them all.

Dr. Jacobi answered Mama's request promptly. Emily and her mother were invited to come to her office.

On the lecture platform or acting as hostess at her daughter's party, Dr. Jacobi had seemed magnetic, but remote. In her office Emily sat just a couple of feet from her and this time those keen, dark, intense eyes seemed to be probing, close and warmly, in and around and behind every word Emily spoke. *She not only knows what I am thinking*, flashed through Emily's mind, *but she knows things about me I'm not even aware of myself.*

"You wish to go to college, Emily? Tell me why?" was all she had asked.

"I need to earn a living. That's the first thing," the girl said bluntly. There was no point in pretending this was sheer idealism, or that she had some lofty goal of raising the standards of women's rights. "It's also true that I want to go— very much. I love studying for its own sake and I'm not afraid of competing with others; in fact, competition seems to be a spur to me and I do my best when it looks as if

I haven't a chance to win or am up against particularly difficult problems."

She had brought with her all her very excellent grades
from Miss Brackett's school and they rested on the desk in
front of Dr. Jacobi. Emily made a slight motion of her hand
toward them.

"Miss Brackett thinks I have a decided bent for scientific
studies; on the other hand, she also feels that I have done well
in literature and English composition, so that I could become
either a teacher or a nurse. I think I should like to become
a nurse."

"Why?" The doctor's head was bent as she examined the
school records.

"My daughter has always been exceptionally capable in
taking care of the younger children when they were ill. I
can't explain her interest," interjected Mrs. Dunning.

"I think," said Emily, "I've had this interest since I was
eight years old. Mama almost died then in giving birth to my
youngest brother and when I saw how the doctors and nurse
worked, how their skill saved her life, it seemed to me that
nothing could be more worth while than nursing. And I've
never altered that feeling." She blushed, thinking this was an
emotional, not an academic, reason.

But the woman doctor smiled at her with great pleasure
and warmth. She spoke seriously, but with an odd tenderness.
"So you wish to be a nurse? You are only a child. You are
too young to know what you really want to do yet. Go to
college and get a good scientific training, and I predict that
when you graduate you will go on to the study of medicine
rather than nursing."

Emily saw the startled look on her mother's face. This was
more than Mrs. Dunning had expected. Even for the girl,
the idea was too new to seem real—that she should become
a *doctor* instead of a nurse.

"What college would you recommend, Dr. Jacobi?" asked Mrs. Dunning.

"I would recommend Cornell University, upstate in Ithaca, New York. There are two men there—Dr. Burt G. Wilder and Professor Simon P. Gage—who are working out what I consider to be the best medical preparatory course in the whole country. Cornell would be best. When Emily is ready to go, I will give her a personal letter of introduction to Dr. Wilder."

They thanked her for her time and trouble, but when they were out in the street Emily protested.

"I couldn't go to Cornell, Mama. It would mean leaving home—with all the added expenses of living at the college. We had both thought of some college here in New York, some woman's college for nurses. Cornell is impossible."

"Do you want to go to Cornell, Emily?"

"Of course. Dr. Jacobi says it is the best, but—"

"Then you shall go." Mrs. Dunning picked up a fold of her long, sweeping skirts in one small gloved hand as she stepped off the curb to cross the street. No matter how simple her clothes, she carried herself with such an air as to seem elegant. "We came to the best person and we wanted the best advice; it would be a mistake not to take it. For the same reason, I'm going to write to your Uncle Henry. No one knows more about Cornell University than he does."

That was true. Henry Sage, together with Andrew D. White and Ezra Cornell, was one of the founders of Cornell; it was deeply close to his heart and he was the one who had been the most stanchly determined that women should be admitted, along with men. It was a radical thing to do but he was determined. He had built Sage Hall as a dormitory where women could live while at Cornell. Yes, his advice would be excellent.

They wrote to him and he answered by arriving a week later.

It was a Saturday and Amy and Emily were in Gramercy Park, just around the corner from their house, reading and enjoying the sunniness of a fresh spring day. Will came to get them, his face troubled. "He is pacing up and down, Emily, and he says he won't talk about your going to Cornell until he sees you."

Her heart sank. Determined as Mrs. Dunning was, she was used to taking counsel from men and going by their advice. Suppose Uncle Henry said she shouldn't go?

They hurried home. Emily took off her cape in the hallway, smoothed her hair and led the way into the gray parlor.

Uncle Henry was, indeed, pacing. Up and down, he strode, his great white, perfectly groomed beard jutting out in front of his chin, his eyes—usually so pleasant—now frosty and cool. "Well, Emily," he said, as she entered and he walked over to take her hands, "what is this I hear about you? Do you have any idea of the seriousness of what you are contemplating? Do you know how the world will judge you for this—this rash thing you are proposing?"

He watched her keenly as she answered. All the family had gathered around; they all watched her. "If by 'the world' you mean some of our friends, Uncle Henry, we already know what they think. Poor Mama has been much criticized. Going to college, they say, will coarsen me, make me masculine. Or else they pity me and say the brainwork is too much for a girl. And if I survive it, I will become odd and peculiar. I don't believe anything like that will happen. I will be different, yes, but not less human."

She was surprised at her own boldness. Talking to Miss Brackett, to Dr. Jacobi, to the family, about college had helped to clarify her thoughts and make her words precise.

He led her over to a sofa and they sat down. He shook his head. "I don't like it because you are so pretty, Emily. There are still very few women students and you will be surrounded by young men. I don't like the thought that you might lose

your head over them or they might lose theirs over you—
youth and beauty don't go with serious studies." He leaned
back. "This is an important matter for me. I have fought
for girls to be admitted on an equal basis, take the same
examinations, stand up to the same amount of hard work. A
failure—any failure—yours, perhaps, Emily—would be just
what our enemies want. It could damage or ruin our whole
program of admitting women students. Can you do it—the
work? Strenuous, hard, grueling work, with just as much of
a single-track mind as if you were ugly and had nothing to
distract you?"

Emily had had many nicknames; none of them had stuck.
Not until many years later, during World War I when the
word "blitz" came to be known, did the family find just the
right one to describe the way she sometimes suddenly flared
into quick, passionate, vehement speech. From then on, she
was nicknamed "Blitzie."

She blitzed Uncle Henry. "I don't care how hard the work
is!" She sprang to her feet. If she was being rude, she didn't
care. "I know I can do the work if I have the chance! As far
as my looks go, I am not a silly, addle-pated girl. Not one of
us is a flirt, not with three brothers around to make us toe
the mark!"

Young Ned let out a whoop, which he hastily covered by
a cough.

Emily didn't hear. She was in full sweep of her feelings.
"As for whether or not I am a good enough student—today
Miss Brackett told me that if I go to Vermont with her this
summer, to study under a new teacher she has hired, I can
make up *all* of next year's work and be ready for Cornell
this fall. Just in a few months. And she would not say that
if I were not a student."

"She would not; that is quite true. Miss Brackett's reputation as a scholar and teacher is extremely high. Fine reputation." Uncle Henry folded his arms and his eyes were no

longer frosty. They twinkled as they looked at the fiery
Emily. "So she thinks you can do an entire year's work this
summer. Hmmm."

He got up and patted Emily's shoulder. He walked over
to her mother's chair. "Mrs. Dunning"—they were related
only by marriage and he always spoke formally to her—"I
like Emily's spirit. I am going to help her get to college. I shall
give her her tuition and what is more, I shall keep an eye
on her for you."

I shall give her her tuition—it was an out-and-out miracle!

They were used to an Uncle Henry who visited them
often, gave them good advice, told them wonderful stories
of how he had worked hard as a young boy, in a country
store, to support his widowed mother and sisters and brothers;
how he had made his fortune out of the lumber business. But
never before had he given the Dunning family any money.
He was a firm believer in "sink or swim." He had become
fond of the Dunnings only because Mama had asked for no
financial help—and did not sink.

That night it was lemonade but the same toast—"To the
family." And Emily added from a full heart, "To Uncle
Henry and Cornell."

By the end of the summer in Vermont, Miss Brackett was
more than satisfied with Emily's work and could give her
credit for having fulfilled a whole year's work, even in Greek.
In September of 1894, when she was eighteen, Emily Dunning
entered Cornell.

Ever since she was eight, Emily had been responsible for
other people. She was the oldest daughter. It was natural that
her mother had turned to her for the most help, the sharing
of the family troubles and confidences; as a result, the girl
had grown a little old for her years and a little too sober in
her thoughts.

All of this dropped off her shoulders like an outworn cloak
the moment she became a college student, responsible for no

one but herself. She was a young girl. She was free. She was in a college that was new, adventurous and young at heart.

The work was hard and demanding, but not at all too hard for her. In fact, so well had Miss Brackett taught and so well had Emily studied, that there were freshman courses she didn't need to take. "If you continue as well as you have started, Miss Dunning," she was told, "there is no reason why you should not complete the four-year course in three."

A nurse's training would have been even shorter but Dr. Jacobi had been right; within the first weeks of college Emily knew that she did not want to become a nurse and care for the sick; she wanted to be a doctor and a surgeon and heal the sick.

Uncle Henry agreed. He would back her, pay all her tuition. Emily had proven his fears all wrong. Not only was she a top student, able to keep up with the best of the men students, but she could take all of the male insults—and the flattery—in stride, laugh at them and go her own way.

She met both her very first day at Cornell. She had come out of a class and, having a few moments free, had stood looking down with delight at the town of Ithaca below and the beauty of Lake Cayuga, the rolling hills, the dark green trees, the richness and grandeur and beauty of the setting. Cornell University was so new that its own planted trees were just saplings, its own buildings raw brick and plaster, but they did not take away from the loveliness of its surroundings.

While she was standing there she heard footsteps behind her and the voices of two young men.

"Look at that," drawled one. He was not referring to the view. "There's one of those silly women students. *Students!* None of them will last six weeks. It's a scientific fact that a girl's brain isn't fitted for this sort of thing. Why can't the fools stay home where they belong?"

She was meant to overhear and her cheeks grew warm.

His friend's tone was even more contemptuous. "She's probably one of those ugly females who hates men because of it and she's out to show us she's as good as we are." He sighed. "Well, we have to take the bitter with the sweet. I had a choice between Cornell and Harvard but I wanted Cornell because it's bold and experimental and new, not set in its old-fashioned ways like Harvard."

"All the same, they're carrying their experiments a little too far, letting women in. I know Oberlin in Ohio and Ann Arbor in Michigan have admitted women for some years, but Cornell's the first school to make it an open rule and actually say these females have the same rights we have."

Emily turned. She was both embarrassed and angry. Before she could open her mouth to speak, they saw her face. Their own expressions changed remarkably.

"Well! A beauty! Maybe, Jim, this isn't going to be as bad as we thought. I wouldn't mind having her sit next to me in class."

Her anger faded and her sense of humor, so strong in all the Dunnings, came to her rescue. After all, the one called Jim was no older than her brother Will; his hair was the same color as her brother Ned's. She had a hunch, too, that this Jim was stupid. He had been in her anatomy class that morning and had failed a very simple question. These weren't ogres; they were ordinary young men.

She laughed. Emily had always had an infectious laugh but now that she was free and starting on her great adventure, her laugh had taken on a new quality of gaiety. "So you think I won't last six weeks? I'll make a bargain with you." She spoke directly to the Jim who was in her class. "If I last the six weeks and you don't find me weeping and asking for special considerations, we'll be friends."

Her comradeship won them. They smiled sheepishly. They hadn't expected either the feminine charm or the direct, blunt manner. Whenever Emily or Amy or Margaret had looked coy or simpered or practiced flirting with their long eyelashes or pouting their pink lips, their three brothers had teased them so unmercifully for it that they never did it a second time. Once was enough.

So she spoke straight and looked straight, friendly rather than flirtatious. It was just the right note to strike. At the end of the six weeks she had forgotten her lightly spoken bargain but the boy called Jim hadn't and he said to her after class one day: "Miss Dunning, you are much better at remembering all the bones in the human body than I am. Would you mind if we studied together sometimes?"

And during that first year she had as little trouble with the rest of the men students. She quickly became accustomed to their first stare of shock, the first contempt or the first smirking gallantry, and then the quick change in them and their acceptance of her.

Some of the other girls had more trouble. In Sage Hall where they all lived, she heard complaints from a few which astounded her, although most of them took the situation as much in stride as she did.

"The men are so rude!" wailed one fluffy little thing. "I dropped my pencil the other day and not one would pick it up for me."

Emily's only comment was, "I've been studying the muscles of the back and shoulders. Yours are fully capable of letting you reach down and pick up your own pencils."

Another girl affected a swaggering, mannish walk and a tailored suit that was unbecoming. "Just let any man try to pick up a pencil for me! I'd soon let him know where he stood with me. I'm just as good as they are. I should think you'd be ashamed, Emily, to let them carry your books for you as if you were an old-fashioned clinging female, and smile and flirt with you."

"I like it. I like good manners in anyone and if they offer to carry my books, why not? Just because I am a student doesn't mean I'm not a girl. I intend to have as much fun as possible, as long as it doesn't interfere with my grades."

Since Emily had already proven herself a better student than most, her critics were silent. Many of the girls felt just as Emily did and among them she made fast and good friends; like her, they worked hard but they weren't going to pretend to be anything but what they were—young, alive, thrilled by this new experience.

Emily did well in her basic language courses that year, though she did even better in the scientific ones. She learned the fundamentals of chemistry; how to handle a microscope and prepare the specimens for study under its magnified glass; zoology in which she learned the varied structure of animals— leading up to anatomy and the study of that most fascinating animal—man.

She was true to her goal. She was among the top of her class, but she was also learning to play the way a carefree young girl should. There had been plenty of time and plenty of games in the Dunning household but she had always entered into them with one eye on her younger sisters and brothers, to see there were no accidents or scrapes. Now she was on her own, with no one to watch.

When the snows came and Lake Cayuga froze, everyone, including the professors, took a holiday. Sleds were dragged out and the floor boards covered with straw to keep their feet warm; they piled into them regardless of age, sex or status and off they went to the lake. The horses that drew the sleds had bells on their harness; the crisp, tingling air, the jingling of the bells and the laughter; the shouts and the singing that went from sled to sled. . . . All these were sheer joy to Emily. She would never forget them.

Somehow, skates would be found for those daring enough to try the lake. Emily wobbled at first and a dozen young men sprang to help her. When she grew more skillful, she skated first with one and then another, liking them all, giving her whole heart to none, but finding this one thrilling because he was so handsome, that one because he made her laugh, the next one because he was a shy young man.

"Conquests" provided the most fun of all, the capitulation of some of the most arrogant of the men students who had said in the beginning they would have nothing to do with the females.

And when they skated on until evening and the stars came out and Emily's cheeks turned pink from the cold, she could pretend that it was the warmth of a man's gloved hands on hers, as they skated, that was so welcome, not the man himself. It was a harmless pretending and in that way she kept her head, in spite of all the flattery and attentions and compliments that were whispered to her on the dark lake. There weren't many Cornell girls, yet even if there had been more, Emily Dunning would have been a belle.

Studies grew more intense in the sophomore year. There was a course in bacteriology, given at the Veterinary College where they could study the bacteriological causes of diseases in animals and understand that this same—or other—bacteria could cause death to humans. The professor was courageous and he taught his pupils to handle test tubes of these killer germs carefully, safely, but handle them they *must*.

The worst ordeal in her three years came the day when Emily was called upon to dissect a cat. She had long ago understood the necessity of operating upon animals. It was the only way for a student of the human body to understand the human body; a doctor or surgeon could never heal or operate unless he could "see" beneath the human skin exactly where the muscles, the bones, the nerves were placed and how they functioned.

To know this was one thing but to stand before the class and dissect was something else again. She had a natural, normal squeamishness which only years of practice would finally overcome before she could handle a human corpse without fear.

That day was far off. This day she took the cat, chloroformed it expertly so that it died painlessly. At this point she was interrupted by a question to the professor from another student.

"Sir, why is it necessary to examine a perfectly healthy cat when we are going to study disease? Maybe I'm exceptionally fond of animals but I know I wouldn't feel too bad about chloroforming and killing a cat that was ill and about to die, anyway. Why must we work on these healthy ones?"

The same question had occurred to Emily and she was glad of the question and the interruption.

The professor settled all her doubts about what she was doing. "Before you students come to the study of pathology, which is the science of disease processes in the body, you must first know what is healthy and normal. How can you tell if a tissue or a muscle *is* abnormal unless you first see it in its normal functioning state? How can you diagnosis a heart condition, where the heart gets too little blood, unless you first have seen how the blood circulates properly?"

The attention of the class reverted to Emily. Her qualms about what she was doing had disappeared. This was necessary. What she was about to do was for the greater good and progress of humanity. The death of one cat might mean the saving of hundreds of human lives.

Her only problem now was how well she could do the job.

The men students had fully expected Emily, no matter how much they had grown to like her, to display some womanly weakness. She might turn pale or faint or cry. She did neither. The one thing they had not counted on was that a woman's hands, accustomed to the delicate use of scissors and stitching, and art of turning under the tiniest of small hems of baby dresses, would naturally adapt themselves to the delicacy of dissection even better than most men.

She cut beneath the skin and with the narrowest of strokes exposed the muscle. The professor called upon her to describe what she saw; when it was finished another tiny, deft stroke revealed the muscles of leg and thigh.

Emily forgot where she was. In that moment was born a passionate interest in surgery and she had taken a long, long step from student toward becoming a doctor-surgeon. To her it seemed incredible and fascinating that there in her hand she could actually see the hidden workings of muscles that moved a knee and enabled a creature to walk.

In her mind and imagination came that transformation that marked the truly dedicated medical personality. She was not seeing an animal—she was seeing a human being lying on a hospital bed with a knee where the muscles had been torn away. Here—and here—and here was where those muscles must be repaired. In that kneecap were the bones and this was how they must be reset so that they could once again move so that a child might play again or a man be able to work or a young girl dance once more.

At the end of that class, when Emily had finished her dissection with an astounding memory of everything she had been taught and the clever skill of her hands, the other students accepted her, fully, as one of themselves. Even when they spoke scornfully of women doctors they didn't mean Emily. She was *their* own exception.

She acquired more admirers. Sometimes they became too eager and then she had to fend them off. It would have been so easy at this point for her to have had her head turned by compliments or become infatuated with one of these young men, but some bit of instinctive wisdom—and the debt she felt she owed Uncle Henry and her family—kept her untouched and sensible.

Besides, she was working hard. She had combined her freshman and sophomore years into one; when she went back to Cornell after her first summer vacation she was a junior.

There were a couple of sophomore courses she had to make up so she just tacked them onto her already full schedule. It was considered a very difficult feat—going through Cornell in three years—and she was regarded with awe because of it.

It wasn't too hard for her quick brain. She had plenty of time left over to make friends, to go rowing on the river with the other girls and walk through the autumn woods with young men and to learn to ski in the wintertime. And this was just as well. The years ahead of Emily Dunning were going to demand the last ounce of strength and courage she possessed, so life was giving her this pleasant interlude.

If sometimes it all seemed too pleasant, if the compliments of her teachers on her work and the compliments of young men on her beauty were about to make her vain, there were always Uncle Henry and her family. She was flying high but one wing was firmly supported by the Dunnings in New York and the other by Henry Sage in Ithaca.

Uncle Henry made his home near the Cornell campus. He entertained the heads of the departments and the president and deans of Cornell, and Emily was invited to these evenings. She would come away from them remembering what a great debt she owed her uncle, not only for the tuition money but because he, more than anyone else, had made it possible for women to be admitted to the college and he had given her this chance.

The least she could do was to keep herself steady and heart-free and work harder than ever.

During summer vacations she saw her own family again. Mama was working harder than ever, taking in more paying guests; both Will and Harry had their hearts set on becoming dentists; Margaret had fixed her eyes on Vassar. Amy and Ned had not yet decided. But they all had the same drive she had, the same dedicated ambition. Right now, she had the opportunity. She must do her best with it so that their turn could come soon.

In her senior year she had to make another decision. She was going to become a doctor, but what kind?

Emily assessed herself. She had the stubborn determination and stick-to-itiveness which would have made her a good researcher and scientist. Did she want that? No. Not for her the isolation in which the scientist must live working endlessly in his laboratory to study disease and find the bacteria or the chemical compounds to cure disease.

She loved humanity too much, even at this age. Behind every test tube she saw the sick patient on his hospital bed. Her hands were unusually gifted in handling instruments but they also had a gentleness which would have been wasted on a thing of metal or glass. She belonged in a hospital. She would become a doctor or a surgeon and the next years would tell her which.

Cornell offered only the preliminary courses. After that there would be more years in some medical college and then one or two more as an intern in a hospital before she could consider herself a real doctor or surgeon. There was time yet to decide.

The junior and senior years went by all too fast for her. When graduation approached she deliberately let down the pace of work. Emily had no fear of the examinations. She knew she would do well. So she skimped, a little, on the studying and stayed outdoors on the campus, went for walks, sought out her friends. The spring days were glorious and she ran off to the lake every chance she could get. She haunted, one by one, her favorite spots with her favorite friends.

She was storing up memories and building a reservoir inside her of these joyful moments. What was ahead of her she didn't know, but something whispered that there might not always be this beauty or this joy.

Her Senior Ball reached the peak of sheer enchantment. Her mother and Margaret and Amy came up to Ithaca for it and Emily had the intense pride of seeing her mother stand with Uncle Henry among the distinguished faculty members. And both her sisters turned out to be the surprise belles of the evening, each in her own crowded circle of young men.

As for herself, she whirled from partner to partner, her long, blue silk skirts spinning fanlike around her feet; the music thrummed in her blood, her blue eyes shining, her fair hair coming a little bit unloosened from the upswept coil and curling about her cheeks. The flowers at her waist were from one admirer; another brought her cool ices to eat. Still others jostled one another to bring her a glass of punch.

She enjoyed it to the full. The ball was the crowning glory of three happy years and she had distinguished herself by her work, too. She had done well in the examinations. Uncle Henry and her family were proud of her, very proud indeed.

3

Cornell had given her just the preliminary background to her medical studies and now she must find a college of medicine for the advanced years. She had always known there was no such college which would accept women; she would have to go to the Medical College of the New York Infirmary for Women and Children. She had known this, yes, but in the bold and optimistic atmosphere she had become accustomed to in Ithaca, she had kept the thought of it out of her mind.

Now she had to accept it and it distressed her keenly. The men among her fellow students were going on to such places as Harvard or Johns Hopkins. She was segregated. She was to be shunted off into the only kind of corner where a woman could learn to be a physician.

Emily came down off the rosy clouds and viewed her position soberly. She had selected a career in which women were not wanted.

The schooling offered by the New York Infirmary for Women and Children was not to be scorned. It was a brave venture, that college, run by the faith and hope of brilliant women, with little money, little support, the most meager of facilities. The Blackwell sisters, Elizabeth and Emily, had founded it just because women could not be accepted into the big medical colleges, and they tried hard to keep its standards as high as those of the men's schools. If brains and ability could be counted, then it did have a high standard. Women doctors like Dr. Anna Jacobi taught there.

But brilliant minds were not enough. When Emily enrolled she found the laboratory rooms shabby and the equipment inadequate. There just wasn't enough money; no rich endowments from private individuals were available and no allotments from city or state, such as the men's colleges had.

She missed, too, the stimulation of male minds and the male point of view. Even more serious, her teachers—like Dr. Jacobi—had only women and children in their private practice, and the New York Infirmary, where the students had their bedside instruction, was only for women and children. This would have made no difference except that the women of New York came to a woman doctor or to a woman's hospital only for pregnancies or some special disorder that only females had. Otherwise, in any ordinary disease or for any ordinary operation, most of them preferred a male doctor and a "regular" hospital.

This meant that Emily and her fellow students—all women, of course—were deprived of the experiences of actually seeing and working with most diseases and complaints. Their teachers could give them information on tuberculosis, for example, only as they knew it from books.

Well, if this was the best she could get, Emily had to make the best she could of it.

She studied harder than ever, even though her professional pride was deeply injured. She had determined to become a doctor on a par with any man doctor, but how could she under the circumstances? There was only one way. She plunged herself headlong, from early morning until late at night, into books and laboratory experiments, into pathology, chemistry, advanced anatomy and physiology. She sat in her classes, her notebook opened and her pen racing, trying to absorb every word and fact and idea.

At home she studied far into the night. Dear Amy had

taken over the task of "assistant" housekeeper to Mama and so Emily was free to devote her time almost solely to her books. No one, not even Mama, ever said to her: "Don't study so much—don't stay up so late—you're working too hard."

Hard work was no novelty to the Dunnings. Even when they saw that she was losing weight, becoming finely drawn, that the softness of her cheeks was changing so that the graceful bone structure was visible and that she had so quickly lost the youthful exuberance of the year before, they did not pity her.

Stubbornness . . . stick-to-itiveness . . . a phenomenal capacity for hard labor—these things all the Dunnings possessed and took for granted. That extra gift of brains which luck and heredity had infused into them only made them feel they ought to work hard to deserve it.

So they were casual about it when Emily's lights burned later and later in her room.

Harry wandered in one night. He watched her for a moment as she wrote and drew diagrams from one book, then he picked up another—a great, fat, heavy one.

"What's this? Gray's *Anatomy*," he read. "What a monster of a book."

She sighed, pushing her hair back out of her eyes with a tired gesture. "That's just what it is, Pads. A monster. Every single bone in the body is in there and I must learn every one of them—and every joint and ligament and muscle. Glands, the circulatory system, the heart, the digestive organs—everything. I look at the description in there of the brain and I wonder how mine can possibly hold all that."

"You'll get it all." He wasn't unsympathetic, just confident.

He sat down to read Gray's *Anatomy* and for a while there was quiet in the room as Emily went on writing. Harry turned pages until he found one that interested him.

"Emily," he said suddenly, excitedly, "this is fascinating.

It's all about the bones of the jaw and the face and the fore-head. You know, a dentist should study this just as a doctor should. Suppose both jaw and teeth were broken, why couldn't a dentist learn to repair them? I think it is a job for dentistry, even if my boss wouldn't agree with me. All he knows how to do is fill a tooth or pull one."

"Dental surgery?" She looked at him, surprised. There was no such profession then, as far as she knew. "If you want to borrow the book, go ahead. Study it as much as you want to, when I'm not using it."

"Thanks." Harry turned to leave and tried to put the big book in his jacket pocket. It wouldn't fit; when he pulled it out he pulled out another, too—a thin, cheap, paper-covered notebook. Emily reached down as it fell on the floor and picked it up.

She opened it. "What is this, Harry?" she asked.

"That's my account book. You know, expenses and in-come."

Income, she read—$2.00 a week. Then, in the opposite column—Treated the girls, 25¢. Gave Emily six ties, 30¢. Two window panes—60¢. Gave Margaret carfare to the country—60¢.

Tears came to her eyes. She turned the pages. Later on he had proudly chronicled his raise: Income—$2.50. Still, the expenses went gallantly and monotonously on as he had taken that small income and given it—most of it—to the others. Gave Mama $5.00. That must have been some emergency and the money was out of his tiny savings. Repairs to bicy-cle—50¢. Treats for the girls—40¢. For Amy—50¢. And so it went, on and on.

No complaints from Harry—or from Will—that they should work so hard and turn over almost everything to the family, yet both were trying hard to save, penny by penny, tuition money for college.

"Harry, if there is any book here you want to borrow,"

she said, keeping her face and her brimming eyes away from him, "please feel free to use it. I mean that sincerely."

"Why, thanks," he repeated, wondering a little at her emotion.

In a few months even that big Gray's *Anatomy* was not such a monster to her; she worked her way through it, little by little, and she had an excellent memory. She was ready to take it in with her when she started work in the dissecting room.

Because she had had previous experience at Cornell, she was more fortunate than many of the other women students. This was their first time to be confronted with the examination of a dead human body. They recognized the necessity of it—no book, alone, could teach them exactly what a shoulder muscle looked like or the shape and function of a heart, unless they saw that muscle and heart with their own eyes. But it was a disastrous first experience for some of them, while Emily could go rapidly and surely to work without flinching.

To her, the human body was, as she said, "the greatest handiwork of the Creator." She had no feeling of horror of the dead, only a sense of the marvel for the human body, and how important this dissecting laboratory was for the student-doctor.

During that spring of 1898, when Emily was twenty-two, the outside world had its own serious problems which were to affect the close-knit Dunning family. The Spanish-American War was declared in April. Young men of Will's age were needed; a patriotic fervor swept over New York and Will enlisted to go to Cuba.

Luckily, the war was not of long duration and the fear that kept its grip on the family turned into a joyful celebration when Will came home late that fall. The victory parade swept close to their home and they all joined the crowd, thrilling to the music of the bands and watching, watching closely as the sailors of the U.S.S. *Yankee* marched along under the Washington Square Arch and up Fifth Avenue. And—yes!—there was Will, safe and sound.

But Will himself had seen too much to be thrilled. He had returned a serious and purposeful man. When he could get Emily alone he said to her, "Don't let anything stop you from becoming a doctor, Emily. You don't know how much doctors are needed. I saw—I know that more men died of disease in this war than ever stopped a bullet."

That fall, too, in her sophomore year at the Medical College of the New York Infirmary, there came the historic day when Dr. Emily Blackwell called the whole school together for an important announcement.

Cornell University was going to open its own Cornell University Medical College. This would not be just the preliminary courses it already gave at Ithaca but a full-fledged medical college as well equipped, as well-taught as any in America. And since Cornell's constitution—bless Uncle Henry and Ezra Cornell and Andrew White!—allowed women to attend, Dr. Blackwell was closing her school. All of her girls were to go to Cornell.

It was a magnificent gesture of sacrifice. She and the other women professors had built this college out of nothing, by sheer toil and faith and with their hands and their hearts. Closing it must have hurt Dr. Blackwell but she was willing to do so because her students would have, not better teachers, but better equipment to work with and better laboratories.

"What is even more important," Emily told her mother, "we will be receiving our bedside instruction inside the hospital wards of Bellevue!"

Bellevue. No wonder Emily went about in a state so exalted she could neither eat nor sleep.

That enormous city hospital of Bellevue had had its origins before New York was ever New York and while it was still New Amsterdam and the Dutch had ruled it, not the British.

At that time, it had been a tiny hospital and an almshouse for the aged poor; it had grown spasmodically in its first hundred years; at times flourishing with an enviable record when fine doctors had something to say about its management; at other times sinking beneath a load of corruption when city officials ignored the doctors and used it for a political football or as a means of enriching their own pockets. At times, it had been so bad that doctors had to stand guard to see that politicians did not steal the very sheets out from under the patients and, in the name of economy, attempt to throw insane patients, diphtheria patients and women in childbirth into the same ward.

Because of the splendid doctors and in spite of politicians, Bellevue Hospital had grown so that now, in Emily's day, it was of mammoth proportions. It was a city hospital, intended for the poor of the city who could not afford the private hospitals.

In all of the centuries of its existence the poor had made their way to its doors; coming by carts when they were too weak to walk, hobbling there, leaning on the shoulders of friends, walking there, crawling there, knocking to be admitted night and day. Because of their vast numbers, the doctors found themselves dealing with every possible kind of disease and wound and mental disorder.

Treating so many kinds of diseases and having to perform so many kinds of operations had stimulated Bellevue's doctors, bringing out every talent in them and forcing them into bold new experiments. Since the 1700's, these doctors were frequently also teachers in medical colleges and they fought to bring their students into Bellevue so that the young men would have the benefit of seeing an operation performed and of examining a patient and listening to their teacher's diagnosis of an illness.

So Bellevue had become, not only one of America's largest hospitals, but one of its largest training grounds for students.

At first students came only from Kings College, soon changed to the College of Physicians and Surgeons, part of Columbia University. By 1891 there was a Bellevue Hospital Medical College, offering students a three-year course and the facilities of the hospital; then it merged with the Medical College of New York University.

The merger caused a storm of protest among some doctors because they felt the medical faculty of New York University was not on a par with Bellevue, and, in protest, several of the professor-doctors of the old Bellevue Medical College asked Cornell University to take a hand in this and establish a college and clinic in New York.

Now there were three medical colleges demanding to be allowed to bring students into Bellevue and have the use of operating amphitheatres and laboratories and to observe in the wards. There was only one solution: Bellevue was already divided into four divisions, even though there was central authority, so why not let the different colleges take over different divisions? Physicians and Surgeons–Columbia was to have its medical men take over the First Division and its students worked there; Cornell was in charge of the Second Division (and two of its professors also ran the Fourth Division); and the merged University–Bellevue Medical College had the Third.

In addition, doctors from St. Luke's, New York, Presbyterian and Roosevelt hospitals, sent their graduate students to work at Bellevue as interns if they could pass the examinations. So Bellevue was the goal, the mecca, the common meeting ground of medical schools from all over New York.

This was the first time in history, though, that there would be women medical students at Bellevue.

There had always been medical nurses. In the early days these had been women drunks, serving ten-day sentences in the prisons and pushed into the hospital wards to work out that time; appropriately, they were called the "ten-day nurses." After the Civil War they had an entirely new type of dedicated nurse. Patients were used to them; doctors leaned on them and the candy-striped uniforms of the nurses were a familiar sight at Bellevue.

A woman student-doctor was quite a different proposition. And it was not until 1912 that the walls of prejudice finally tumbled at Bellevue and a woman physician was finally to be appointed to the staff.

That was in the distant future. Right now, in 1898, Emily and her fellow students were the pioneers.

Whatever feelings the men students of Cornell had about "those damn women"—hostility, resentment or amusement—they had little chance to show them. They were just too busy. The new college was on Twenty-eighth Street and First Avenue, directly across from Bellevue, and the students' lives flowed between the two at a breathless pace.

Even those few students who had an unusual sympathy for the ambitions of the women had no time to give them anything but an encouraging smile or a friendly word.

As for Emily, she noticed neither hostility nor sympathy. It seemed to her that she had no interest left in young men. What was a handsome young face compared to the emotion she felt for the elderly, lined, careworn face of a brilliant teacher? How insignificant to her was the memory of a silken dress and flowers at her waist, waltzing to music in a ballroom when she now had the privilege of walking into a laboratory and beholding its chaste, severe, functional beauty?

The laboratories were temples; the tables were like altars. The pure emotion in Emily, as she bent over microscope or test tube and her fingers moved to adjust a lens or turn down a flame, was the rapture of dedication to the goddess—Medicine.

She felt it even more strongly when she went across the street to the hospital and met with a small group to follow one of Bellevue's prominent doctors on his rounds of the wards.

Here was the whole reason for her dedication. Here were the patients. On either side of her, as she stood by the hospital bed, might be two very healthy, vigorous young men, fellow students, and she hardly knew they existed. Her ears heard only the voice of the excellent Dr. Lammack, and her eyes absorbed every detail of the ravages of typhoid fever on the patient in front of her. Books had told her what to expect of typhoid fever but Dr. Lammack used this patient—kindly and with courtesy—to show how carefully the doctor must examine each single patient and not expect each one to be alike. "The typical textbook case," he would explain, "is recognized easily, but such a case will usually be found in the textbook rather than at the bedside."

It was a warning she would never forget. Books could teach her what was typical; human beings varied in a thousand ways from the typical.

He instilled in her a careful habit of examining the patient very thoroughly, for a long time, before deciding what the trouble was. He would say: "Nine-tenths of our mistakes in diagnosis are made by not looking and only one-tenth by not knowing."

Because no sick person was ever turned away from the doors of Bellevue, no matter what the ailment, the student-observer had an opportunity to study almost every possible kind of disease or pain or injury. One day Emily might watch Dr. Lammack. In the days following she would watch techniques in the receiving room and see how quickly doctors sprang to work on an accident case, or she would watch the techniques and procedures of the outpatient department, set up to take care of those minor ailments where the patient did not need to take up bed room in the hospital.

It was the very drama of life to her when she saw a doctor examine a patient with a supposedly mild stomach-ache and then see the doctor hesitate, examine more closely, ask more questions. She stood on tiptoe to see the examination, looking over the shoulder of the student in front of her.

"What would you prescribe?" the doctor asked one of the students, who stammered that he didn't know—a stomachache—perhaps some sodium bicarbonate or a mild purge.

Emily was saying over and over to herself: Appendicitis! She had seen the patient wince when the doctor had touched his right side. And the doctor confirmed her thoughts.

"It's the appendix—we'll keep this man for observation to see what develops. It may have to be an appendectomy. Didn't you notice the slight pain?—and didn't you see this?" he went on to elaborate.

Little by little, month after month, year after year, she was taken or permitted to go into every department of that vast, vast structure which was Bellevue. Into the outpatient clinic, into the male wards, the female wards, the children's; into the isolated wards taking care of tuberculosis and the contagious fevers, the typhoid and yellow fevers, even shown a rare case of cholera.

And at last, at last came the time when Emily was to sit in the huge circular ampitheater, on a bench that rose in a tier behind the one in front and watch a surgeon down below do a complicated, dangerous operation.

She was attracted to surgery far more than to the study of medicine.

Fortunately for her and her classmates, they had entered their medical training at a time in history when the old ways of centuries were exploding with new discoveries. The old methods, both of treating the sick and operating, had become completely changed.

A method of anesthesia had been found so that the patient no longer had to suffer the operation fully conscious, and the doctor no longer had to operate with lightning speed.

Louis Pasteur in France had found that germs caused fermentation and changes in wines and milk. These germs were to turn medical theories completely upside down. Reading about them, Dr. Lister of Scotland saw immediately that it was these very germs which were causing infection in open wounds. Also that the surgical instruments carried germs from patient to patient, often causing poisoning. He worked until he found an antiseptic—carbolic acid—and immediately surgery emerged from its Dark Ages into a sure and positive science, and he became a benefactor of mankind. Now surgeons could perform operations they never dreamed of before, because their clean knives carried no germs into the body during the operation and carbolic acid also kept the patient germ free afterward, during the healing time.

On the strength of this new method, new kinds of surgery were being attempted all over the world.

As for diseases, Pasteur had spurred Koch to the discovery of the tubercle bacillus; Roux found an antitoxin for diphtheria—and so it went.

It was a dizzy, wonderful time in which medical students were living, but it was also an extremely difficult time. No sooner had Emily mastered three pages of a book describing the only cure and treatment of a disease than the professor told the class to scrap what they had learned; a new cure had been found, a new germ discovered, a new diagnosis made.

For two years, her sophomore and her junior years, Emily had no life but that of Cornell Medical College, Bellevue Hospital—and home. She rarely ever went out to a concert or to the theater; her only recreation was a brief walk in the park or the walk from her home to the hospital—and even that was time she grudged from her studying.

The Dunning household resembled a school, in those rooms which the family kept for themselves. Will had come home from the war determined to go to college and become a dentist. He had found a good job with good pay, and with hours arranged so that he could enroll immediately in the Academy of Medicine. It might take him years to graduate and become a dentist but he was on his way.

In his room at night he studied. Across the hallway Emily studied. And in between the two, Harry wandered, borrowing books from both. He knew exactly what he wanted— Cornell University first for a sound medical background and then the New York College of Dentistry. Emily's books and Will's books were giving him a good head start. Margaret was working with Miss Brackett, preparing herself for Vassar; Ned had his homework.

Amy was proving herself an even better manager than her mother. She had stepped into Emily's place as her mother's confidante and strong right arm. She had a natural flair for making a home charming and pleasant.

Financially, the Dunnings were better off. The rooms of the paying guests were seldom vacant, and Amy saw to it that the money from them stretched far. Emily had an unexpected stroke of luck, too, in getting work during the summer vacations.

Dr. John Rogers was in charge of student problems at Cornell Medical College. He was a young man himself; very young for the job, highly skeptical that his women students would ever succeed in their chosen profession, but willing to give them all the help he could. When a request came to him from Dr. W. C. Gilley for an assistant as summer replacement in the Center Street Dispensary, Dr. Rogers gave Emily Dunning first chance at it.

Dr. Gilley may have been doubtful at first, but by the end of the first day's work he was more than satisfied. She continued to work for him every summer, all the time she was in college.

The dispensary didn't handle major surgical cases—only minor ones such as a sprained ankle to be bound, a broken bone to be set in splints or plaster of Paris, a boil to be lanced. Dr. Gilley taught Emily to be as exact and careful with these minor things as if she were performing the most delicate operation, and, in turn, he was delighted with the natural skill of her hands. She was one of the few students who could wrap a bandage to suit him.

So in the summers she not only earned money but gained priceless experience.

By the time she was a senior she had spent several years thinking only of medicine, dedicated only to her studies. She did not know just exactly when it was that she first became aware of an intrusion into that world, at just what moment she first noticed a very tall young man with broad shoulders, who seemed to be forever coming into a corridor just when she did or opening a door for her just as she was about to pass into a classroom or a ward.

He was just *there*. He was not in any of her own classes or she would have recognized him by name or face. No, he was a stranger to her and, in the beginning, just a vague one. Then, one day he slowed his steps as he passed her. She looked up and saw by the expression in his gray eyes that she was no stranger to him.

With an instinctive feminine gesture which she had not used since those days in Ithaca, Emily straightened the belt of her skirt, touched the collar of her blouse to be sure it was not wrinkled, reached a hand up to tuck back a straggling curl.

That afternoon, she was rushing as usual to go from one part of Bellevue to another. She had to cross a narrow bridge over some excavations being made on the grounds, and before she knew what was happening she bumped squarely into the gray-eyed young man. In the next second she realized it was no accident; he had been waiting there for her and he was standing there, blocking her way, smiling at her.

"I believe you are Miss Dunning?"

"Yes, I believe I am Miss Dunning." She smiled, too, at

his rather formal question, and mocked it with her formal answer.

"Well, I am Ben Barringer and I have been anxious to meet you. I asked one of the fellows in your section to introduce me, but he was so slow I couldn't wait, so here I am."

Here he was. It was as simple as that. It would be too much to say that Benjamin Stockwell Barringer had already fallen in love with Emily Dunning, just by watching her in the hallways and corridors and perhaps it would be too much to say that Emily was in love by the time they crossed that little bridge together—but it happened almost as quickly as that.

She had kept her heart and her head and her single-track devotion to medicine free until now; those years had served their purpose. She had been wrong, though, if she thought she could forever do without love, and now she fell in love just as completely, as fully, as she did everything else.

Six-foot-tall Benjamin Barringer and the lovely Emily Dunning were as perfectly suited to each other as two people could possibly be.

They walked for a few moments that day and talked; they met by accident again the next day and by no accident at all, the next and the next. They found both were Cornell students though they had never been in the same classroom at the same time, nor in the same group which met with a doctor at Bellevue. Both had the same passion for their work and the same dedication. They had the same sturdy physical health and tremendous capacity for work.

Even their differences complemented each other. She was inclined to narrow her interests too much to one drive, while he had a variety of interests—sports, art, the outdoors—and he introduced her to all of them. He was more the scientist-researcher-discoverer than she, and would have preferred the laboratory, while she thought first, and always, of the patient, the sick man or woman.

He had a far more contradictory nature than she. Emily

fell in love with those contradictions. He had been an out-
standing athlete, a member of his football team at New York
University from which he had been graduated Phi Beta
Kappa. He had the size of the football player, with an unexpected gentleness and tenderness of heart.

His gray eyes could be cool and remote one moment as he
spoke of a problem in medicine; gay with humor the next
moment; ardent when he spoke to her of his love—and
dreamy, off in his own private world, when he was looking
at a landscape or a sunset.

"I wanted to be an artist," he confessed to her. "I still paint
for my own pleasure, but my mother thought that doctoring
was a more stable career for me. She didn't want me starving
in a garret some place."

She met his father, Theodore Bame Barringer, who was a
public school principal, and his mother, also a teacher, and
liked them both, instantly. Her own family accepted him
wholeheartedly and liked him, once they got over the shock
of the realization that Emily was no longer completely theirs.
They had to get used to hearing it constantly on her lips:
"Ben says—Ben thinks—when I see Ben—Ben and I—" She
was the first of the Dunnings to make the break from their
tightly knit circle. From now on she would be loosening one
tie after another with her family and building them, one by
one, with Ben.

They could not think of marriage yet. That was understood. They both had to finish medical college, graduate with
the title of "Doctor." And even then, there would be two
years of internship ahead of them in some hospital. In all
that time neither would be earning enough money and marriage must wait.

Though they had fallen in love quickly and had settled
the question of marriage almost as quickly, Emily knew there
was one question that had to be answered first.

On an evening when, for once, Emily and Ben had the gray

parlor to themselves, she dared to ask the question. It was late winter, the weather had turned colder and they sat together on the gray sofa in front of the blaze in the fireplace, one hand of hers held tightly in his.

"After we are married, Ben, and you are successful in your practice, will you expect me to stop being a doctor and stay home to be a housewife?"

His head jerked toward her in surprise. His gray eyes reflected his astonishment. "No, of course not. Why should you stop being a doctor, unless you chose to? How could I ask such a thing of you, any more than you would have the right to ask it of me?"

In her relief she was half laughing, half crying. "Do you know how unusual a man you are, Ben Barringer? Another man might have said that, to spare my feelings, but you really mean it. You really feel that my career is as important as your own."

"I certainly do. Haven't you worked just as hard, sacrificed just as much? Haven't your records shown you have the brains? Why should I want to deprive the world of a good doctor just to selfishly keep you at home all to myself? Besides, how could I talk over my problems with you if all you wanted to talk about was the soup you'd made that day or the new curtains you were planning?"

She leaned back, contented, picked up an apple from the bowl beside her and began to eat it. There was just no way of explaining to Ben how rare a man he was, how lucky for her that he did not have the typical male attitude of the year 1900.

He was thinking of something else. "What about your career, Emily? What hospital do you have your eye on for your internship? You can't put it off. You must be thinking of it now. You'll have to be preparing for it and putting your application in."

She admitted she had been far too busy to give it much

thought. "Besides," she said bitterly, "I haven't much choice. There are only a few hospitals which will take women and those are not the big hospitals, the ones I want. I will have to intern somewhere, in a woman's hospital I suppose, where there are only women and children patients."

"Ridiculous," he glanced at her.

"It's worse than that. It is barbarous. It's cruel. We women seem to be allowed to go so far, then an inch farther, and then the door is slammed in our faces. Oh, yes, we can now get the same medical training as men—which wasn't true before— but not the final training, the actual hospital practice which permits us to deal with all kinds of diseases and perform all kinds of operations. No, there the door slams. I should like to *kick* it open! I want to intern in one of the city hospitals!"

She put down the apple and turned to stare at Ben. He was staring at her just as hard. "Why not?" he asked, softly.

"I could try!" she answered. "Tell me, Ben, what does one do to prepare for the competition to get into one of the big hospitals, like Bellevue, for example? As a doctor-intern? How do you go about making application?"

He was only one year older, twenty-five to her twenty-four, and young enough to believe with her that even if there wasn't much chance of succeeding, it was worth the challenge and the try. His handsome face was filled with excitement. "Most of the big hospitals hold competitive examinations for internships," he told her, "but they're tough. Graduates from medical colleges all over the country want to get into the big hospitals, so the first thing you have to do is get into the 'Hospital Quiz.' It's an accelerated program of review and it's tough, but it has to be tough to get you ready for the written and the oral exam you'll have to pass. These hospitals accept only those who pass the competition with the highest grades."

"I'm going to try, Ben."

"Good for you!"

When she walked with him to the door, the first flakes of

snow were falling. The little belt-line horse-drawn trolley was coming up the street and Ben ran to catch it, turning to wave just before he swung aboard. She closed the door, thinking how lucky she was to have Ben behind her so solidly at this critical moment in her life.

Margaret passed her in the hall. "Mmmm . . . perfume . . . your best satin blouse . . . and *my* best patent-leather belt! No question about it; my sister is in love. How does that fit in with being a doctor?"

"It fits perfectly," Emily answered softly.

4

Once again Emily took her problems to Dr. Anna Putnam Jacobi.

"I've already spoken of this," Emily explained, "to some of the professors at Cornell—to Dr. Lewis A. Stimson, the professor of surgery, and to Dr. William Metcalfe Polk, the dean, who is also professor of gynecology. Both of them, in the past two years, have expressed themselves as satisfied with my work and I know they like me. But all they could say was that it had never been done before and that it could only be put to the test—and that would be at the very end of my senior year."

"I see. You would be putting all your eggs in one basket. You would deliberately *not* apply to one of the women's hospitals but prepare and take your chance that they will let you compete with the men for a 'regular' hospital?"

"That is it precisely, Dr. Jacobi. I might very well be turned down—I probably will be. All the hospitals, including the women's hospitals, will have filled up every vacancy and I will be left with the title of doctor and no place for me."

Dr. Jacobi might have said: Don't waste all these years of study and work by trying for the impossible. Be satisfied with what you have. But she herself had never been satisfied. She had once challenged hidebound prejudices. Some years before the Boylston Prize competition, sponsored by Harvard, had ruled that no paper submitted to it should be signed. So she had entered a paper on a highly original idea. Her paper had won first prize and only then was it revealed that it had been written by a woman.

She was a fighter. "Women physicians," she said now to Emily, "need these hospital opportunities and it is only by going out and trying to get them that they will ever succeed. Women must be willing to go up, to be knocked down again and again, before the general hospitals will finally be opened. You have had especially worthwhile preliminary training, and you must enter this fight."

But if she failed, as she likely would? To which Dr. Jacobi replied, "Then I should like you to come to work with me as my assistant, for a year. When the next year's examinations come along, you can decide if you'll try again or intern in a women's hospital."

It was a generous and wonderful offer. All that Emily had to do now was to "enter this fight."

The first step was to get into the "Hospital Quiz." She went to see Dr. John Rogers and talked to him about it. That night she met Ben, as she frequently did, for a short walk before he had to go to the night school where he was teaching to earn his own tuition money.

"What did Dr. Rogers say?" Ben asked her immediately. He was only a student himself and could help her only by his encouragement and interest.

She hesitated and then blurted out: "He—he swore at me! He said—'Hell, Miss Dunning, what do you want to take that for?' I've never had anyone swear at me before."

Emily had expected Ben to be indignant but he laughed. Then he grew serious. "Perhaps Dr. Rogers did that on purpose, to see your reaction to swearing. Because if you get into this Quiz course, Emily, you'll just have to get used to swearing. Everybody in there is tense; they are driving themselves furiously; if they don't know the answer to a question, they don't get a second chance. So Dr. Rogers may have been testing you. If you get upset by swearing, or you made a disturbance about it in the class, they wouldn't let you in. How did you react?"

"I didn't turn a hair," she said proudly. "It was a shock but I wasn't going to let him see it. I just told him that I wanted to take the course to prepare for hospital examinations, along with all the others. Then it was his turn to gasp."

"But did he agree?"

"On one condition—that if any man in the class ever objects to my being there—that is, if any student registers a real complaint that I am hindering the work, then out I go."

The next day Ben was waiting for her at the classroom door of the Hospital Quiz. Perhaps the sight of his big, broad-shouldered figure walking beside her and the look on his face quelled anyone's first impulse to ask: what's *she* doing here? Dr. Rogers taught the class and his manner helped, too. He was perfectly matter-of-fact. "Will you sit over here, please, Miss Dunning?" and then he swept quickly into the lesson for that day. There were no incidents. No one raised any objection.

She soon realized why the students swore. Their nerves were on edge. So much depended on how well they did in this course. Their future was at stake and their tempers were short when they failed a question.

Dr. Rogers' sole purpose was to review everything they had learned and to point out their weak points. Questions were fired at the students, and the answers had to be rapid and accurate. If they hesitated or rambled they were cut short and the professor went on to the next student for the answer. Sometimes, when words alone would not reveal the answer, he made them demonstrate.

"The bones of the foot and ankle," he announced one day in class, "come on up here, Miss Dunning, and demonstrate."

She walked up to the platform, scarcely able to hide her astonishment when young Dr. Rogers suddenly whipped off his shoe, put his leg up on his desk and waggled his foot in front of her. When he said "demonstrate" he meant just exactly that.

But she was equal to the situation. By now she realized she could expect anything to happen in that class. She grasped his foot, naming the various bones, twisting the foot now and then to show the class a better view of ankle or toe.

From then on, she was one of the class. She drove herself as hard as they did, studied as hard, asked for no special treatment, blushed at no mention of the body—and the men students made no complaints at her being there.

The question of which hospital she should apply to, which one might be most likely to allow her to compete, could be postponed no longer. The time was growing short.

The first five hospitals she wrote to promptly refused to consider her. The only reason given—but enough for them— was that no such thing as allowing a woman to compete had ever been done before.

Dr. Jacobi next suggested Mount Sinai Hospital since she had many friends on the staff. It was one hospital, too, that had permitted a woman gynecologist, a Dr. Josephine Walter, to serve on its staff, many years before. Of course, Dr. Walter had only attended women patients in childbirth and for maladies which were peculiar to women, but it had been an opening wedge. There was no harm in Emily's trying. Dr. Jacobi proved once more that she was in this fight, too. She accompanied Emily on the necessary round of visits to every single member of the medical board of Mount Sinai.

"I think I have a good chance, Ben," Emily told him after a week of such visits. She was tired; there were dark shadows under her eyes and Ben had insisted they take this Saturday afternoon off and go for a horseback ride. Spring was almost there and this was a prematurely nice, sunny day. They jogged along the country trail, slowly, so they could talk. "Everyone seemed sympathetic. Dr. Howard Lilienthal and Dr.

Alfred Meyer are actively behind me and I feel sure they can persuade the others to let me take the examination."

Ben was both glad and apprehensive. "That examination at Mount Sinai is supposed to be extremely difficult—one of the toughest of all."

"I know. Dr. Lilienthal has urged me to study with two doctors as quizmasters because they are familiar with the Mount Sinai exam and will coach me especially for it."

"That's adding even more work to your schedule." But he didn't try to persuade her not to do it. He would never be overprotective toward her and so destroy her courage.

Her horse shied slightly and Emily nervously grabbed at the pommel. Ben laughed. He was a superb rider himself and he was amused at her. "You have the courage of ten men but you're a little bit scared of a horse, aren't you?"

She admitted it and she laughed. "It's a good thing I am going to be a doctor, safe in a hospital ward, and not in some job where I have to ride behind a horse."

It was a good thing she couldn't see into the future.

Emily Dunning now had to carry her full load of regular college work, her bedside instruction given by a doctor at Bellevue, the special cramming in the Hospital Quiz. In addition, she took on extra study hours in anatomy and surgery under Dr. Walter Brickner, and medicine and therapeutics under Dr. Louis Hauswirth. It stretched her endurance to the breaking point, almost, but she felt it was worth it.

In addition to his studies, Ben had his job teaching at night school. They could meet only for rare moments and they planned and contrived so that they could pass through the same corridor at the same time and get to the Hospital Quiz a few seconds early to talk, or she would meet him and walk with him on his way to night school.

They could make do with this because they were young, romantic and optimistic.

Even when Emily was told she must make a new round of

personal visits, this time to the trustees of Mount Sinai Hospital, she was still optimistic. She squeezed in the visits somehow and went to see each trustee personally, at his home or office, to plead her case and ask that she be allowed to compete on equal terms with men.

A couple of the trustees seemed actually to approve. The rest wouldn't commit themselves, but at least they didn't say "no" to her—then.

The blow came unexpectedly. The day for the examination had been set. Emily had come to think that she had nothing to worry about but the examination itself, when she was notified curtly that the decision had been changed.

Mount Sinai would not consider appointing a woman as an intern in their hospital, under any circumstances.

The decision was final, no question about that! Everything in Emily—mind, nerves, heart and spirit—had been geared just for that examination and now she was like a machine still spinning, but without traction and for no purpose. Instinctively, in spite of shock and outrage, she did the thing which was absolutely necessary for her, if she were not to suffer the worse shock of wasted efforts. She demanded of the medical board that, at least, she be allowed to *take* the examination.

Collectively, they shrugged their shoulders. It was a foolish request to them since it could lead nowhere, but perhaps they owed her that much. Permission was granted.

Ben and Dr. Anna Jacobi knew why she had made the request and they approved. They knew she had to salvage some kind of moral victory out of this rebuff or she might have lost courage to go up for another.

When the day of the examination came and the student-competitors filed into the big room at Mount Sinai which had been set aside for this purpose, she found herself all keyed up. No job could come out of this for her; she was running a race for no prize. Nevertheless, she dug just as hard into her memory, flogged her brain unmercifully for the right answers. After the first hour, when she realized she did have those answers, she began almost to enjoy herself.

Only the students who passed highest in the written test were asked to come back the next day for the oral. Emily was one of these and it seemed to her that she did well in that, too.

It was not until many years later that she found out that she had actually passed highest of them all.

In one respect she was very fortunate. Time was growing so very short and she and her fellow conspirators, Ben and Dr. Anna Jacobi, had to think so quickly of other hospitals and other examinations, that the reaction to the Mount Sinai affair—the despair and frustration—lasted no more than a couple of days.

Most of the hospitals had already held their competitions. Ben had already won his place at one of the "Big Four" hospitals—the New York Hospital.

Of those remaining she had to rule out several because she knew she would be refused on purely technical grounds—that the facilities, for example, at Bellevue did not include anything that could possibly be made into living quarters for her. The bedrooms for the men interns were dormitories.

But there was one hospital, a branch of Bellevue, an emergency hospital, which did have a room she could sleep in. This was Gouverneur Hospital, in the heart of one of the city's poorest, toughest slum districts.

Again she made the rounds of the Medical Board of Gouverneur. "Impossible," said one. "The emergency patients brought in there are not polite ladies and gentlemen. Even if they would tolerate you, no nice woman like yourself, Miss Dunning, could possibly work with drunks and drug addicts or listen to the obscene language you'd be forced to hear."

"Impossible," said another. "The nurses would resent having to work under a woman doctor."

"It would just be asking for trouble, Miss Dunning," said another. "The other doctors, the men doctors, would find the presence of a woman on the staff much too upsetting for their work and peace of mind."

Dr. John Rogers had already warned her that this would be her main trouble if she should ever succeed in getting onto the staff of a general hospital. "They would all fall in love with you or hate you," he predicted, speaking of the men doctors who would be her colleagues.

She had two powerful allies, however, on the Medical Board at Gouverneur. The great and eminent Dr. John F. Erdman, chief surgeon of the Third Division at Bellevue, a consulting surgeon at Gouverneur, professor of practical anatomy and clinical professor of surgery, was enthusiastically in favor of women surgeons and particularly in favor of Emily. He determined to convince the other members of the board.

And a Dr. Louis J. Ladin concurred. He, too, worked for her so well that the board finally gave in: she could compete on the same basis as any man. If she placed high enough, she would be an intern at Gouverneur.

Once again Emily walked into a big room with desks, into a room charged with that unbearable tension of a medical competitive examination. Gouverneur could accept only *four* of these many, many college seniors who were crowding in, who had come from all over the East Coast. She saw several of her Cornell classmates, and handsome, smiling Jerry Sheehan waved to her encouragingly. She was surprised and delighted, also, to find another woman competing—Ethel Mayer, also one of her classmates from Cornell.

Emily had been wiser than she knew, when she had stuck her chin out and demanded the right to take that Mount Sinai examination. Although the questions here were different and she had to work just as hard as the others, she had had that trial run to give her a slight confidence and familiarity with examinations.

For hours and hours she wrote, stopping only now and then to conjure up in her mind the right page and description in Gray's *Anatomy*, or to recall exactly what a doctor had said and done as he showed them the treatment of a disease on a hospital patient, or to remember step by step a difficult operation in Bellevue's theater.

When she finished she knew she had done well. She wasn't surprised, afterward, to hear the announcement that she was among the top students and would therefore go for the oral the next day. She was proud that Ethel Mayer had got that far, too, and also Jerry Sheehan. Cornell was doing well.

On the second day, the day of the oral, Emily was nervous. Waiting their turn to be called in, they were all nervous. Only four of them would be chosen, with two more alternates. Nerves were snapping under the strain.

Here sat a student, his eyes absolutely glazed, mumbling to himself: "I can't remember a thing. I've forgotten everything." And here was one feverishly reciting under his breath pages and pages of a textbook. Some couldn't sit still, they had to pace. Others sat numbly. Even the ebullient Irish gaiety of Jerry Sheehan was subdued for once. Emily and Ethel Mayer sat close together for the comfort of each other's presence.

It was a terrible ordeal.

Yet, when Emily was called in, within five minutes all her nervousness left her. They were asking the questions quickly, these members of the Examining Board, all expert doctors and teachers themselves, but they were not firing them at her the way Dr. Rogers used to. She had time to think. Her amazing memory, which she had cultivated by the hardest of hard work, stood her well and the answers came to her tongue, precise and accurate.

Soon she noticed that some of the questioners became more

insistent. She had a feeling they were not keeping strictly to the questions that everyone would be asked. As if it were for their own satisfaction, they began to probe her mind deeper and deeper.

"If a patient were admitted to the hospital with such-and-such symptoms, Miss Dunning, what would be your diagnosis?"

"Diphtheria," she announced promptly. A warning bell clanged in her brain; a symptom had been described that was not necessarily typical of diphtheria. "I would also examine the patient carefully for any possible indications of brain tumor."

There was a rustle of papers and a quick exchange of a pleased smile between two of the doctors; one of them turned to her and said: "Go on. Will you please elaborate on that, Miss Dunning?"

She did. It was an exhausting ordeal which they put her through but she felt no fatigue until afterward. She almost enjoyed it—her brain pitted against their attempts to trap her. And toward the end of the questioning she felt that none of them were trying to trap her and that their insistent extra questioning was being done to please themselves and they were now friendly to her, delighted with her.

When it was all over and she went back to the waiting room to sit with the others, she suffered a letdown. Probably the examiners had not been as friendly as she thought; perhaps she hadn't impressed them. Had she answered that diphtheria question correctly?

The candidates went into the examining room and came out, some looking downcast, others cheerful, others defiant. They knew that only four of them would definitely get places at Gouverneur and that two more would be chosen to stand by as alternates. These last two would get on as interns only if, for some reason, one of the first four could not serve.

Jerry Sheehan came out and passed in front of the bench

where Emily and Ethel sat. He made a grimace and said, "I know I flubbed one question, but I think I didn't do too badly with most of the others." The three of them strolled out into the corridors and, since all were finished with their oral, they could talk about it. Emily realized, as Jerry described the question he had missed, that it was the same one she had been asked, only the examiners had led her deeper into the subject. Her first answer must have been correct.

Finally, the last of the examinations were over. Now they waited for the results. No one could talk; they were too tense. A few could not sit still but most of them sat, dumbly, paralyzed, no longer hoping, just waiting for the ax to fall.

The doors of the examination room opened. One of the doctors came out, carrying a paper. Like a magnet the whole, large group moved toward him, their eyes fascinated by that paper. He tacked it up on the wall and left. There was almost a stampede to read it, to see whose lucky names would be posted there.

Emily and Ethel were caught up in the rush but they could not see the names at first; there were too many ahead of them. Only when those in the front row turned away, shoulders slumped in despair, or shoulders shrugged with an attempt at indifference, could the two women squirm up to the front. If Emily had not been too intent on the paper she might have seen a couple of the candidates glance at her with awe, but she saw nothing until she was standing up front and then the names seemed to dance before her eyes.

She could not believe what she saw. It couldn't be true:

FIRST PLACE: MISS EMILY DUNNING

First place! There was a roaring in her ears and for the first time in her life she felt like fainting. Then someone was shaking her hand. A perfect stranger was saying, "Congratulations, Miss Dunning—congratulations." Edith Mayer was beaming, as much for her own good fortune as at Emily's, because Ethel had placed fifth as the first alternate. Jerry Sheehan had won the lowest alternate, sixth place.

Those who placed second, third and fourth, who would intern with her at Gouverneur, were names she didn't know and she was too excited just then to try to find them.

Besides, she couldn't have found them had she tried. All too quickly they had vanished; those who had lost had gone off to lick their wounds, while those who had won hurried to spread the great news—as did Emily.

Truly there was a great celebration in the Dunning home that night. Ben was there, proud and happy. When he could get Emily alone he let her tell in great detail about the examination, knowing from his own earlier experience how bottled up she would feel unless she could talk about every question, every answer, to someone who understood medical language.

It was the family, the Dunnings, who most appreciated this night, however. The great venture was a success beyond any dreams. Mrs. Dunning was proud; the others were thrilled. Not once did it occur to them that it should matter that Emily now had two years of unpaid work ahead.

The laughter and the talk, the toasts, the cakes and cookies eaten—because happiness can make you hungry!—were countless. The telephone never stopped ringing. Dr. Anna Jacobi and her husband, also a doctor, called to say how thrilled they were. Josephine Goldmark, who had been a classmate of Emily's at Miss Brackett's, called and shortly afterward, Miss Brackett herself added congratulations.

Toward the end of the evening friends began dropping in, irresistibly drawn to the great triumph. Dr. Felix Adler, who was becoming famous as the founder of the Ethical Culture movement came, bringing with him several people, among them Major Edward L. Zalinski, whom Emily had met before, and liked. He was the inventor of the Zalinski dynamite gun and he was a fascinating, though fiery, man, who was spending his fortune from the gun in trying to reform politics in New York City.

When at last it was over and she had said good night to everyone, Emily climbed the staircase to bed. She paused a moment on the step before the landing. Here was where it had all started, that night she had watched a doctor coming in and out of Mama's bedroom.

The next day she and Ethel Mayer met by appointment and went to the Medical Board offices to find out on just what day their appointments to Gouverneur Hospital would take effect. Ethel's visit was more a formality since she would not go to Gouverneur unless one of the top four dropped out.

They were told that nothing could be done until Commissioner Keller ratified the appointments.

Of course. Sometimes the students forgot that Bellevue and Gouverneur were city hospitals and therefore city officials had to sign contracts. The city government was in control of these hospitals and gave only limited powers to the doctors and the Medical Board.

They had the address of City Commissioner Keller. They found it easily; at least, one of the bowler-hatted men lounging in the anteroom assured them it was "Keller's office—sure, ladies, this is the place."

They were both startled. Outside of the world of medicine they were naïve. Maybe this was a typical Tammany Hall politicians' office, full of spittoons and spitting men; blue with cigar smoke, dirty, the floor slopped and sticky where beer had spilled on it, but surely the official who would put his stamp on their appointments deserved a more dignified office.

Nor was Commissioner Keller the man they thought he would be. He sat in front of his old roll-top desk, littered with paper, a cigar stuck in his mouth, and looked at the two trimly clad young women with a sour, suspicious face.

"Commissioner Keller," said Emily, "we have come to ask

about the ratification of our appointments and to find out just
when we begin work at Gouverneur Hospital."

He turned his swivel chair halfway around in his irritation,
then swung back to face them. "I will not ratify your appointments."

"But—"

"I will not be responsible for having a young woman doctor out on that ambulance service and have her break her
neck."

This simply could not be happening. Emily had given considerable thought to the dangers of the ambulance service at
Gouverneur; she knew she would have to ride the ambulance
but she also knew she could do it. "We are willing to risk our
necks, Commissioner. We've taken all the risks and problems
into account."

His face turned sour and mulish. "I tell you *NO!*—and I
mean that. I will listen to no more words on the subject.
That is final."

It *was* final. Stunned and incredulous, Emily stared at the
man and understood that he had refused her. He had the
power to do so. Not all the doctors or medical boards could
make him change his mind. This petty official could and had
taken away the position she had earned with all her hard,
exhausting work.

The defeat was so smashing that she and Ethel left the office
in silence, while behind their backs the Commissioner smiled
with bitter pleasure. He had stopped all this tomfool nonsense and these newfangled ideas.

The two women separated with nothing more than a few
broken words to try to console each other. What was there
to say that would be of any comfort to them?

Emily walked slowly homeward. The memory of last
night's celebration was unbearable. It was equally unbearable
to think of anything else—Ben's pride in her, her long years
of struggle, the hopes, the courage, the attempt and failure at

Mount Sinai, the oral examination yesterday, that notice announcing: First Place—Miss Emily Dunning—

She made herself look at the people who passed by. A woman walked in front of her, using little, mincing steps, pulling a child by the hand, and both were well dressed. *Bustles are going out*, Emily thought. *And hats have large plume feathers.* A beer wagon plodded down the street, six magnificent white horses, gaudily decorated, pulling the heavy weight. And behind it a dainty carriage, with a young woman, holding a parasol over her head . . . there was a store on this corner and Emily remembered there was a telephone there she could use.

She called Ben.

"What is it, Emily?" He was alarmed by her voice.

"Ben—" she started to speak and then, uncontrollably, she started to cry.

By the next morning, however, she had regained courage and poise. During the night she had remembered the words of Dr. Jacobi and had repeated them over and over to herself until they became a sort of charm that would keep her going: "Women must be willing to go up, to be knocked down again and again, before the general hospitals will finally be opened." Well, Emily Dunning was just another one of the casualties; someday someone *would* succeed.

Graduation from Cornell University Medical College was at hand. After what she had already gone through, the examinations, the final ones, seemed easy, and she had the consolation on graduation night of hearing her name called out as second on the Honor Roll and that she was the winner of a hundred-dollar prize.

A hundred dollars was a great deal of money in 1901.

Emily Dunning was now Dr. Emily Dunning. She was twenty-five years old. In the fall she would go to work as assistant to Dr. Anna Putnam Jacobi and in the meantime there was a summer job for her with Dr. L. Emmet Holt, at the summer branch of the Babies Hospital in Oceanic, New Jersey.

It was a good thing for her to get away from the city for a while and not be reminded, by a hundred little things, of her terrible disappointment. She learned a great deal, too. Dr. Holt was a specialist in children's and babies' diseases and she picked up from him much that could not be learned in books.

This was true, also, when she became Dr. Jacobi's assistant that fall. The brilliant woman doctor—and how strange it seemed to Emily that Dr. Jacobi should now formally address her as "Dr. Dunning"!—had a passion for meticulous, careful diagnosis and equally so for watching the progress of a treatment. Her standards were the highest. She impressed upon Emily her own care for the patient—never to relax vigilance, never to take anything for granted.

Emily considered herself fortunate to be working under a mind as great as Dr. Jacobi's. She found, too, that the diseases and the preventive care for the health of women and children had a special fascination for her.

This should have consoled her, as she was determined it would. She was also earning money, which would not have been true if she had been an intern at Gouverneur. And it was some comfort to know that since both she and Ethel had been removed from their winning places, at least it was a fellow student at Cornell, Jerry Sheehan, who had been moved up. If someone had to profit from their misfortune she was glad it was the friendly Irishman.

The deep regret for Gouverneur settled to the bottom of her mind and stayed there. The Dunnings didn't cry over spilt milk. Like Dr. Jacobi, she would try to learn to forget herself and help some other girl to get that chance she had missed.

Other people had the same idea. Emily Dunning had come so close to it; with a little extra luck, a little help, perhaps one of the girls from the next graduating class at Cornell could make it.

She had a letter one day from the Reverend Percy S. Grant, her family's pastor at the Episcopalian Church of the Ascension, on lower Fifth Avenue:

> 7 West 10th Street
> New York City
> October 28, 1901
>
> My dear Miss Dunning:
>   I was so glad to have your mother tell me . . . that you were to be with Dr. Anna Putnam Jacobi. That will give you a very good standing in New York and also plenty of experience.
>   It seems to me, however, that something ought to be done in this city to secure for young women graduates in Medicine the hospital practice which was denied you. Won't you talk this matter over with Mrs. Jacobi? I should like to know what ought to be the point of attack in bringing about a better state of things. Whether it would be wise to make an attempt at some one hospital or, indeed, what you both think of the matter. . . .
>   With heartiest best wishes.
>   Yours most sincerely,
>   Percy S. Grant

The letter did not surprise her. Nothing that the Reverend Grant did, in this way, could surprise her. He was gaining a wide reputation as being a fearless leader in civic and social reform.

New York City needed reform. It was filled with political corruption, political bribery; the politicians had both hands deep in public money while they did nothing to get rid of slums or improve charities or build hospitals. Nellie Bly, a reporter on the New York *World*, had shown up the disgraceful, horrible conditions under which the insane were treated, by getting herself committed to Blackwell's Island, pretending insanity. The Reverend Parkhurst had formed a powerful committee for public reform.

Emily's own friends, Major Zalinski and the two sisters, Josephine and Pauline Goldmark, were working hard for social, political and economic reform. Josephine and Pauline were members of a remarkable family; one sister married Felix Adler of the Ethical Culture Society; another married Louis Brandeis who was many years later to be a judge of the Supreme Court of the United States. Josephine and Pauline were working now with Florence Kelley in setting up the National Consumer's League.

With such fiery, determined people behind her, Emily felt that solid support could be rallied to any of this year's Cornell women who wanted to compete for posts in the general hospitals. A new mayor was in office, a good, reform mayor, Seth Low, and to him Emily wrote a long document listing all of the reasons why it was advantageous to the hospital to have a woman doctor on their staff, and why it was so advantageous to the woman herself. She did a masterful job on that report.

Next she talked to the Cornell women students, begging them to draw up a petition to Mayor Low.

Her mistake, she knew, had been to ignore the politicians and appeal only to the doctors. The new women applicants, candidates to the general hospitals, should not make that mistake but clear it first at the very top, at the Mayor's office.

The women students were reluctant and nothing was done about the petition, but the Reverend Percy S. Grant continued his pressure directly to the Mayor and in getting favorable publicity in the newspapers. There had been newspaper editorials when Emily was denied her rightful place last spring, and several of them had been shocked at the injustice.

The campaign went on and Emily began to worry. It was now early in the spring; if the women students were to be allowed their chance, something would have to be done quickly: there was not much time left to apply.

Then one day Emily was in Dr. Jacobi's office when a thin package was delivered to her. Inside was a short letter from one of the Cornell students, Nan Gilbert Seymour, which read:

> Dear Miss Dunning:
> Enclosed is the famous document which you wanted to see. I hope you will be properly impressed! Please return it to me when you have finished with it. . . .

The "famous document" was an official announcement by Mayor Seth Low that the competitive examination at Gouverneur Hospital would be thrown open to women that spring; that if a woman won a place it would be given to her, with the stipulation that she would have to accept such an appointment on the same terms offered to the men with no exceptions made in her favor; the services offered would include the internships of one year of general medicine and one year of general surgery, with a year and a half of ambulance duty. The woman physician would reside at staff quarters in Gouverneur Hospital.

Emily took the paper and went into Dr. Jacobi's inner office, brandishing the document like a torch above her head. "Look at this, Dr. Jacobi—it is a complete triumph!"

The older woman took it and read it, then she glanced thoughtfully up at Emily. "How do you feel about this? Does it make you feel bitter about last year?"

The answer came promptly. "I feel little resentment for last year and absolutely no jealousy for the lucky girl who will get that place at Gouverneur this year. You taught me that. Who do you think will win?"

Dr. Jacobi seemed to be listening intently as Emily discussed the various women students and which ones seemed to have the best records and the best qualities of stamina and which would likely win. She *seemed* to be listening, but she was not because she suddenly interrupted Emily:

"Doctor, *you've* got to take that examination."

"*I* take it?"

"Yes."

"Why, I couldn't possibly do it this year! I am not pre-pared; it is necessary to be at a highly competitive pitch to think of entering that examination which is open to the best students from all over the country." Emily could hardly be-lieve that Dr. Jacobi was serious. Such a thing hadn't occurred to her. "No, I am out of the race this year."

Dr. Jacobi was obstinate. "You are not out of the race," she replied. "You have got to take that examination—and all your experience of last year will help you more than you realize."

5

Emily argued and argued. The discoveries of germs and of Lister's antiseptic methods of surgery had meant that all kinds of new operations were being performed. Neither she nor Dr. Jacobi had given more than scant attention to them. Dr. Jacobi's practice was that of a physician, not a surgeon. The medical journals of this country and others were full of new theories, new ideas, which college students would be studying and memorizing. Emily had not had that chance.

To all the arguments Dr. Jacobi only answered, ". . . nevertheless, you have got to enter that competition."

In one sense she was right and Emily understood. It was almost a moral obligation. The prize had been fraudulently snatched away from her, and the position at Gouverneur was rightfully hers. Was she to stand aside and let someone else have it? This meant submission to something very wrong.

Worn out by the arguments Emily finally agreed. But the difficulties seemed to her to be too enormous to cope with.

She talked them over with Ben and her family. She was asking a great deal of her mother and her sisters and brothers; they had already made sacrifices for her and now, working for Dr. Jacobi, she had been in a position to repay and to help the others go to school. If she should win at Gouverneur, it would mean two years without pay and the family would have to provide for her during those two years.

They responded without any question. She must try!

And Ben said, too, "You must try! I know how difficult it will be for you. Last year at this time you were at the peak of your form. You had spent years on study and memorizing and you'll be competing now against students fresh from their classrooms and books, but I still say—you must try."

For two days Emily felt as if it were all unreal and that it couldn't be happening to her. One moment she was so excited she was ecstatic; the next, she felt like a fool. However, she found herself being pushed along by Dr. Jacobi, who released her from any further work and insisted she again get in touch with Dr. Hauswirth and Dr. Brickner, as special tutors.

The moment Emily started to study with them, she faced reality. The enormity of what she had undertaken was like a cold bath and she saw her position with clear and unromantic eyes. She would have to study as she had never before thought possible—and she had thought she knew what study was.

Since she had left college whole textbooks had been revised. Methods, treatment, diagnoses which she had learned she would have to unlearn and then memorize the new ways. In addition to this was a complete review, again, of all she had forgotten. This she must do in just a couple of months.

She studied while she was dressing; she studied while she ate. She cut down sleep to six hours a night and mumbled words in her dreams. Even so, she knew that there was no question but that the brightest students who would be competing from the finest medical schools in the country would beat her. They were trained for just this competition while she, naturally, had relaxed that special razor-edge condition of the mind during this past year.

There was only one chance and only one. If she could squeak through the written test, then her practical experience as a doctor with Dr. Jacobi would give her some odds during the oral.

Dr. Emily Dunning filed her application and her letters of recommendation; she was duly admitted as a candidate for the Gouverneur Hospital competitive examinations.

Now there were only two weeks left. Reviewing material she had already learned was not too difficult, but it was exasperating. She knew what the answers were but she had forgotten the exact, precise wording, commas and paragraphs. As for the new material!—two months were just not long enough to learn it all.

The day of the examination came and it was just as she feared. Over half the questions dealt with methods and theories she hadn't had the time to learn thoroughly. When she went home afterward, Emily knew she hadn't done badly —much better, in fact, than she had had any right to expect— but in competition with student-candidates from Johns Hopkins, Harvard and Cornell, primed to their finger tips, it was doubtful that she had placed among the top.

Her mood was not of failure but of rebellion.

The next morning, when Dr. Henry Mann Silver, chief of the examiners, telephoned her to say: "Miss Dunning, I am sorry to tell you this but your paper was not quite good enough. As you know, we select only the very top applicants to come back for the oral, practical test. Please believe me, I regret having to tell you this"—something broke inside her.

She had one of her very rare temper outbursts. Her nerves were raw. "Dr. Silver—it is unfair. You know it's unfair. Last year I passed highest. I've already proved my fitness for the job at Gouverneur. Is it my fault that a year has gone by and I have not had the opportunity of preparing as the others have?"

"No, Miss Dunning," he admitted. His voice sounded surprised. "I agree with you. It isn't fair. From that standpoint, your written paper yesterday was surprisingly good. Basically sound—"

"The only questions on which I did not do well were those so new they had not come up in *my* college training. I'm being doubly penalized. I was robbed of the position last year, and now I am expected to know new theories and methods I've had no chance to prepare for." She was being rude. She was speaking to Dr. Silver as she had never dreamed she could, but in her anger she didn't care. "I don't think it means I am any less a doctor. I could have shown you, today, in the practical test what I have been doing this year and how much valuable experience I have had."

There was a long pause at the other end of the line. Then his voice came, thoughtful, and very much astonished. "That is quite true. You have been working under Dr. Anna Jacobi, haven't you? A fine physician. Well, that makes it all the more difficult for you, Miss Dunning, and again, I want to say how sorry—"

She hung up on him. It was an awful thing to do, a very childish thing, but it made her feel slightly better.

She put down the telephone and walked slowly to her own room. The whole family were away on a special holiday. Mrs. Dunning had worried about leaving her alone during the competitions but Emily had insisted that they go. Now she wished they were back. A desolate, end-of-the-road depression settled over her and she couldn't even call Ben to talk to him; he was at work in his hospital.

In her room the first thing that struck her eyes were her books on the shelves and scattered on the table. Notebooks. Half-scribbled pieces of papers. Anatomical drawings. A pencil flung down on the desk. Days and nights she had spent in here. Every book and paper mocked her with the hopes she had had.

She threw herself on her bed and cried and cried and cried.

The tears would not stop until she was weak and spent and shaking. Then she rolled, listlessly, over on her back and stared at the ceiling and wondered what was to become of her now. She couldn't ask Dr. Jacobi to take her back. Besides, working with her meant no chance to practice surgery.

All of the other hospital appointments were already made for the year. There was no place for her to go.

Again the tears came, and she let them slide down her cheeks and didn't raise a hand to wipe them away. From sheer exhaustion she finally slept.

The knock on her bedroom door awakened her. It was the maid and she was holding out an envelope. Emily raised herself up, groggily, and took the envelope. "Thank you, Mary," she said. Opening it, she read:

> Numbers increased, report practical examination Gouverneur Hospital 2:15 P.M.
>
> Henry Mann Silver

She was too tired. The words meant nothing. She glanced at the clock and saw that it said 12:30. So they had given her a reprieve and had sent it too late. In her nerve-racked state of mind, she couldn't possibly get up, eat lunch and present herself keen and bright and mentally-alert for the examination.

It was too late! Even if she could pull herself together and get down to Gouverneur, she couldn't pass an exam. She was a wreck, physically and emotionally. She had gone all to pieces.

The telephone was ringing so she forced herself wearily to her feet and went downstairs to answer it. Major Zalinski was calling her to ask how she had come out in the written test of yesterday. He had taken a tremendous interest in her, as well as in the whole political reorganization of the city hospitals.

She told him the whole story: how she had not placed quite

high enough to be included among those chosen to take the test today, how she had insulted Dr. Silver, and how the note had come and that the numbers had been increased and now she was among the top group. She even told him of her breakdown.

Major Zalinski had not been an army officer for nothing. He knew what to do when his troops faltered. "Of course," he said, in his stern, military voice, "you are planning to pull yourself together and go down."

"No, I am through." She meant it. There was no fight left in her.

"Oh, no, you're not; you're going to make an effort to take that examination." Young lieutenants had been known to snap to attention at that note of command from him.

It brought her out of her lifelessness. It infuriated her. She was tired of people telling her she had to struggle and fight on, no matter what the odds. "No, no, no!" she screamed into the telephone, stubborn and fierce. "I am not going to. I am utterly demoralized and it is impossible."

Major Zalinski paid no attention to such mutiny. Calmly, he ordered her to go. He commanded her to go. He insisted.

Again, she shouted: "No. It's impossible. I just can't do it!"

"You get busy at once, pull yourself together, eat a quick lunch and report at Gouverneur at 2:15. No soldier under fire deserts." He repeated what he had said, but this time in words that were stinging and lashing. Major Zalinski knew the caliber of Emily Dunning, knew that if she didn't go she would regret it all her life. She was temporarily demoralized and at that moment the lash was better for her than kindness.

Her anger became rage and her shock turned to fury. How dare he speak to her like that? Had he no consideration for her feelings? Nobody had ever dared speak to her like that! And her rage burnt out every trace of weakness or exhaustion. Her rage was like a fire coursing in her body—but a fire that turned her icy-cold and strong and completely without emotion, except to show him.

"All right!" she said. "All right! I will. I'll go."

Once again that day she hung up when her caller was in the middle of a sentence.

She had little more than an hour, now, to bathe, dress, eat and catch the trolley for Gouverneur Hospital. Oddly enough, in this very unusual, cold, cold frame of mind, everything she did clicked with split-second precision. No fumbling. No hunting for anything; no stopping to think what to do next. Her fingers had no nerves and they fastened hooks and eyes easily and competently. The blouse and skirt flowed over her head and fastened themselves with no trouble. She was a robot.

She even ate something, without any nervousness in her stomach. For once, combing her hair was no trouble. It was soft and fine but today it coiled itself because her hands moved like a machine. She pulled on her gloves and walked outside, and it didn't surprise her in the least that the horse-drawn trolley should be standing as if it were waiting for her.

She walked into Gouverneur Hospital at 2:14, with one minute to spare.

That same icy-cold anger stayed with her all during the examination. She had no nerves, no tremors, no indecisions; her unconscious mind was able to take over; everything she did was absolutely perfect. Her answers came mechanically—but correctly.

When she was asked to demonstrate a point, she did so as if it were the most ordinary, natural thing in the world, and not that she were doing it before judges whose slightest look or word could mean thumbs up or down for her.

She was given a problem. Into her mind almost automatically clicked the sight of the patient, the look of him, the sound of his labored breathing, the appearance of the flush on his face, the smell that went with that particular disease, the loca-

tion of the pain—these were the symptoms and she forgot
not a single one. The treatment? It came to her just as vividly
and clearly.

The performance she gave that day was truly incredible.
Stripped of every fear and emotion except anger, she was like
a machine that had been turned on and the machine could not
make a mistake.

When it was over, the examiners, one and all, broke
precedent by congratulating her. What she had done that day
was as nearly perfect as a human being could do, something
rare and brilliant. And since she was the last to be examined
they could tell her, without her leaving the room, that the
result of this oral test made up for yesterday's failure. They
could not give her first place but she was fourth of the four
chosen for Gouverneur.

She had made it. The other three were men. She was still
the first woman to win, in competition, a place in a New York
City hospital.

Not until she had reached home again and heard the telephone ringing and found it was Ben, did this icy control of
hers break. Telling him the whole story and realizing how
very nearly she had not gone that day, she began to tremble.
"I owe everything to Major Zalinski," she told Ben. "If he
hadn't insisted and made me so angry, I would never have
pulled myself together for that examination."

Ben agreed but he added, "He helped you, but you did it,
Emily. Don't forget that."

As soon as he hung up to go back on duty, Emily called
Major Zalinski. He refused to listen to her words of gratitude,
turning them aside with a bluff and hearty, "Nonsense. You
had been beaten for the moment, but that happens in any war.
You just needed a jolt to bring you back in fighting trim."

The next day the newspapers had the story and newsboys
shouted it on the streets: EXTRA! EXTRA! WOMAN
DOC AT GOUVERNEUR! And people passing by on the

streets stopped to glance at the headlines of this startling event:

WON ON MERIT

MISS DUNNING ON STAFF
AT GOUVERNEUR HOSPITAL

First Woman in America
to be given such an
opportunity

This was on April 24, 1902. For the first time in her life Emily was to have something like a holiday. Two of the four chosen in that competition would start their hospital internship that coming fall, while she and the other successful candidate, a Dr. Batchelder, would not begin until January 1, 1903.

In the meantime she would assist Dr. Jacobi whenever needed, but not every day as before. She had time to be a little bit lazy—if a Dunning could ever relax that much—and see a little more of her family and friends and Ben. She had to begin thinking about the clothes she would wear at Gouverneur and make some arrangements for her sleeping quarters there.

She took stock of her family and was amazed at what they had all accomplished. Will was studying now at the New York Academy of Medicine and courting Ruth Morse, a young Quaker girl. Harry was preparing himself to start at Cornell and Margaret was in her first year at Vassar. Amy had not yet decided what she wanted to do. In the meantime she helped run the house and showed talent for planning small, informal parties for their friends.

Mrs. Dunning was still the center, the life force, from which they all drew steadiness of purpose and the weapons of courage.

The district where they lived had changed. It had once been a fashionable residence, now artists and actors and writers were beginning to move in and create around them that atmosphere which became famous as Greenwich Village. Emily and her family liked the change. They liked the feeling that young people around them were stirring and doing great things in the theatrical and art worlds.

Mostly, though, her friends and Ben's were doctors, teachers, or those interested in social reform. She still kept up a close relationship with her first schoolteacher, Miss Anna Brackett, and was pleased that Ben and she got along so well.

They were not much for playing games. They would all rather talk. In an age when a fashionable social evening usually included a game of charades or someone singing tra-la-la at the piano, Emily, Ben, the Goldmark sisters, Felix Adler, Edward Hungerford, a newspaper reporter on the *Sun*, Amy and Harry, Will and Ruth Morse—all preferred to talk.

There was so much to say. A fever ran through them of new things that needed to be done to change the world for the better. Slums should be cleaned out; working conditions should be bettered; medicine and hospitals should be made available to everyone.

Because they were all vibrant people, the talk was never boring. And because they were young, they laughed as much as they talked. Their friends appreciated the quiet twinkle in Ben's expressive gray eyes and Emily's infectious laugh which could start them all laughing. The hardships of the past few years were forgotten and her sense of humor had a chance to romp. She would tease Josephine Goldmark about the pigtail she had worn at Miss Brackett's and the long, black stockings which all Miss Brackett's girls wore—and hated.

This period in Emily's life brought her closer than ever to Ben.

On his days off from hospital duty she could almost always arrange to be with him. As they strolled through the streets of New York, his sense of color and perspective and art gave her an entirely new picture of what she saw. She needed this. With her single-track mind she was beginning to see people as either one of two things—the healthy or the sick.

With Ben's vision she saw the beauty in an old woman's face, lined with a lifetime of tragedies and joys. She noticed the poetry in motion of a fine horseman cantering up Fifth Avenue.

Horses were something she thought about a great deal in those days. Once she had said to Ben that it was a good thing she was going to be a doctor, because of her slight timidity about horses. Little had she known then that part of her internship would mean "riding the ambulance"—behind a swift, madly careening horse, going as fast as the ambulance driver could make him in order to reach the accident victim on time!

She had told Commissioner Keller that she had considered the risk of breaking her neck and was willing to risk it, but that didn't mean she wasn't still scared.

So whenever possible that summer she and Ben went riding. They would walk and trot their horses until they found a quiet spot in woods or meadows, dismount, and then Ben would unpack his canvas and his paints and go to work. He preferred working in oils but he could content himself with sketching, and Emily would sit beside him and watch. It was a constant marvel to her that this man she loved, with his great athlete's body and his searching, scientific mind, could also have such an artistic bent.

He was a man of many moods where she had the constancy of only a few.

When he had finished painting they would mount their horses once more and ride back, talking of themselves. It seemed to them that from now on their paths lay straight ahead, their internships and then setting up in practice as doctors. The only discouragement in their lives, now that

Emily had won through to her goal, was that they couldn't marry for several years.

This was hard on them. Emily was now twenty-six years old and Ben was twenty-seven. They wanted marriage and a home and children. Luckily, they were disciplined people, both of them; they didn't indulge themselves with neurotic frustrations of what should be instead of what was, and they considered themselves fortunate in that, of all the millions of people in New York, they should have found each other.

This time of peace lasted through October. At the end of the month there was a Halloween party at the Dunning home. It was strictly family except for the addition of Ben and Ruth Morse and it turned into one of the gayest parties they had ever had—because of Ben.

Emily had never seen him in this excited, almost feverish, mood. This was one time they did revert to their childhood and play games; they bobbed for apples in a washtub filled with water and came up with it between their teeth, their chins and noses dripping water; they told ghost stories and tried to scare each other. All during the fun Ben laughed the most and talked the most and was unable to sit still for long, restlessly proposing another and another game.

The next day at dinnertime, Mrs. Dunning and Amy and Emily and Ned could talk of nothing but the party the night before. Except for Emily, they all thought that Ben had been the star of the evening and were delighted to find he wasn't as quiet as they had thought. But Emily was vaguely disturbed. Some instinct told her that Ben had been a little too excited.

Outside the open windows they heard fire engines clanging. Then more of them, distant but ominous. "It must be a tremendous fire," Mama said. "And everyone is running out into the street. There go two more engines!" They crowded to the window to watch the splendid fire engine horses go tearing uptown.

The fire engine horses and the ambulance horses—the pride
of New York—were racing up the street, almost neck and
neck. These horses were specially picked for their courage
and speed and they seemed to know as well as their drivers
that if they got to where they were going in time, they might
stop a tragedy, rescue an injured man from dying, save a
home from burning.

The street was crowded with people watching in mingled
morbid fear and excitement. Bets were laid on which would
get there first: the ambulance or the fire engine. The horses
were racing for all they were worth, their gleaming sides
flecked with foam, their mouths wide open to breathe as they
tore up the street.

Emily shivered. Wherever they were going it was certainly
to a scene of flames and screaming people. As a doctor, she
had a special interest. She leaned out of the window and saw
that the ambulance had the name of Gouverneur Hospital
painted across it.

Could she ever ride that? The little ambulance seemed so
frail, so tiny; it swayed from side to side behind the racing
heels of the horses. The driver cracked his long whip and the
bells jangled. As it went around the corner, she saw on the
open seat behind the ambulance the figure of the Gouverneur
doctor clinging with both hands to steady himself.

In a short while they knew what it was all about. A vast
number of fireworks, belonging to William Randolph Hearst,
which had been stored away in Madison Square Garden, ready
to be used as a gigantic celebration for victory in a coming
election, had exploded—all at once—in one great blast which
had damaged property and set houses on fire and injured a
great many people.

Even after the fire was out late that night, the scene was
horrible. Emily and Amy ventured as close as they could get.
The ambulances kept coming and going, taking away their
pitiful load of injured victims, and once Emily was sure she

caught a glimpse of Ben helping to carry a litter into his ambulance.

She was awakened that night from a deep sleep by the ringing of the telephone, which she recently had had installed in her bedroom so that Dr. Jacobi could reach her at any time. But it was not Dr. Jacobi. "Miss Dunning," said a man's voice she did not recognize, "are you awake? I have some bad news for you, I'm afraid. I would have waited until morning but I thought you were entitled to know—"

"It's Ben." She thought of his ambulance and how near he must have worked to the falling timbers of the burnt houses. "He's hurt?"

"No. He's not hurt, but he is very, very ill. He worked steadily until just an hour ago and then collapsed. I hate to tell you this, but we are afraid it is typhoid fever."

The man who was calling was a doctor; she recognized that much from his professional manner. Her heart froze. Typhoid fever! One of the most dread killers of all diseases. "I'll be right over immediately," she managed to say. "Thank you for calling me."

She had begun to get used to climbing out of a warm bed to go and attend a patient, taking over some of Dr. Jacobi's calls, but never had she thought she would be going on such a fearful errand as this. She was not going as a doctor, yet her doctor's mind worked just the same: If this was typhoid fever then Ben had been incubating the illness for some days and that must have accounted for his feverishness on Halloween.

His father and mother were already at the hospital when she reached it. They were told by a sympathetic fellow intern that Ben had gone right on working and riding the ambulance, ill and dizzy as he was, until he had fallen unconscious.

There was no question about it; it was typhoid fever. He was in delirium and didn't know his parents or Emily when they were finally admitted for a moment to his bedside.

For three weeks he lay there while the fever raged. At moments he was completely rational and himself and then his eyes followed every look and word of Emily's, though he couldn't speak. There was only the smallest flicker of life in those gray eyes. The flesh on his big body melted away until he was nothing but skin and bones, and any little nurse could lift him. The daily treatment was that he be plunged into an icy bath to bring down his fever, and the nurses managed it with no trouble at all, carrying him from bed to bath and back again.

Emily had no hand in either doctoring or nursing him, yet her job was just as important. He wanted her there. He pulled strength from her. And she gave it, not only to him but to his mother and father as well. His brother Ted was already a doctor and he and Emily knew how serious Ben's condition was, but they tried to keep from the others the fact that Ben was close to dying.

Mrs. Barringer finally guessed. She broke down and sobbed and Emily held her in her arms, trying to give comfort and sustenance. They had always been very fond of each other, but from this moment on, a strong tie enveloped between the girl and her future mother-in-law.

On the night of the crisis they all waited together outside his sickroom door. On this night they would know if he would recover or if the fatal complication, lobar pneumonia, would set in, as so often happened with typhoid patients. If it did, in his weakened condition Ben would have no chance.

All night they waited. The doctor was noncommittal each time he came out of Ben's room. Every nerve in Emily's body ached and she felt herself growing numb with every passing hour.

Then he came out, in the gray hours of early morning, and he was smiling. Ben's temperature had gone down. His heart was beating a little bit stronger. A miracle—or his own determined will to live—had won a victory.

"I think we can safely say there will be no complications," the doctor told them. "It will take time and there will be a long, long period of convalescence, but the critical moment is passed."

When she was eight years old a doctor had saved her mother, Emily thought. Now a doctor and the new discoveries of medicine had saved the other person she loved most in the world. Mingled with her relief, her joy, her tears of happiness, was a feeling of sheer gratitude to such doctors and to the world of medicine.

The convalescence was not nearly as long as the doctor had predicted. Ben's youth and his natural virility quickly threw off the effects of the illness. Every day he gained weight. Every day he could talk a little more and he was more cheerful every time Emily called to see him.

When Ben was at last able to walk slowly out of the hospital, his hand on her shoulder, she had the wistful hope that life would be good from now on; that she was finished with near-disasters and could look forward to the next two years of quiet work; *hard* work, but fruitful, satisfying, peaceful and rewarding work.

6

It was late November and time for her to be giving serious thought to what she would need at Gouverneur. Particularly, there was the matter of her clothes.

Gouverneur was an emergency hospital, a branch of the city hospitals of which Bellevue was the center. Patients who needed a long stay in bed for recovery were not kept at Gouverneur but transferred, if possible, by ambulance to Bellevue. The acutely and seriously ill were treated immediately at Gouverneur and emergency operations were performed.

Mostly, however, it was an emergency way station and the ambulance was the shuttle that carried the sick from their homes or the streets to it. The ambulance carried patients on to Bellevue if transfer was necessary, or to other hospitals if it was decided that a patient would be better off somewhere else.

An emergency hospital meant just that—emergency, urgency, quick, sudden calls during the day or night—Emily reminded her mother as they discussed clothes. They would have to forget what was stylish for that day and age and concentrate on what could be put on and off in a hurry.

For the night calls, when she would have no time to dress and must attend a patient inside the hospital, they designed a long, gray woolen robe, reaching almost to the floor, buttoned from chin to hem. They bought high-cut slippers which could be pulled on in one quick gesture, and would cover the ankles. That was part of the difficulty—to get clothes which would be practical and still modest. In the early 1900's women did not show their bare ankles and Emily would have been criticized if she had.

Men doctors had uniforms given to them by the city, but Emily was handed a sum of money and told to provide her own. No homemade uniforms would do. Her appearance must command respect. Since she wanted the best and most professional tailoring, she had a tailor make her a large supply of long white duck skirts, with large and small pockets for all her instruments, and long-sleeved shirtwaist blouses. Over the blouses she would wear short-sleeved, low-necked linen jackets.

That took care of what she would wear inside the hospital itself, but what about ambulance duty? The cap that the men doctors wore was most becoming to her; it was navy-blue, with GOUVERNEUR HOSPITAL spelled out in gold letters across the front of it. That left just the uniform itself, which was the most difficult to achieve.

"I shall have to be jumping up and down off the back of the ambulance and I shall have to move rapidly," She told Mrs. Dunning as the two examined the other clothes, just arrived from the tailor's. "A long, wide, full skirt will hamper me or trip me. But a short, tight one would create scandal and be uncomfortable, too."

Mrs. Dunning was clever about dresses but she was stumped. "I know you want something that suggests a uniform but you don't want it to be mannish, either. And there's the problem of pockets again," she sighed. "I just don't know. For the wintertime, you certainly will need a heavy jacket to go over it."

Emily agreed. "A mackintosh would be best."

For weeks they discussed nothing else. She got Ben to describe the difficulties of ambulance work and this made the situation worse. What she would need had to be light enough for summer, heavy enough for winter; or thin enough material to be shapely and becoming, yet thick enough to stand the wear and tear. The length was a real problem too, for from Ben's descriptions she could just see herself jumping down from the back of the ambulance, in too much of a hurry to look where she was going, catching her heel in the long, full skirt and sprawling in front of bystanders. Above all, she must somehow maintain her dignity, but how? she kept asking herself.

One day, out of the blue, came a letter from a Boston firm, V. Ballard and Sons, Ladies' Tailors. When she and Ben had done lots of riding, Emily had ordered a riding habit from them. V. Ballard and Sons not only remembered her but they had followed her career in the newspapers with pride. They would consider it a great honor and privilege to make, free of charge, the ambulance suit for America's first woman ambulance surgeon.

Would she consider their offer?

"Would I! It's a miracle. I was just thinking I would have to follow Miss Bloomer's crusade and start wearing those big, baggy, short trousers she advocates for women."

"Emily—you wouldn't!" Her mother was horrified.

Emily assured her she certainly never would. She wrote to Ballard's immediately, explained the whole problem and handed it all over to them—the need for comfort, modesty, durability, and how it must adapt to every situation. She might have to run in it; lift a patient; climb up steps (not until many months later did she think she should have warned Ballard's that she would be climbing down a rope ladder into a ship's hold!)—yet it must be stylish and feminine.

Ballard's must have winced when they got those specifications. But they rose to the occasion. When it was done and she went to Boston to try on the finished product, she was delighted.

Made of the finest, smoothest, navy-blue serge with a satin lining, the upper part fitted her to perfection. It nipped in at the waist yet had a faintly jaunty military cut about it. The genius of the tailors had created the perfect solution for the skirt. In the accepted sense, it was not a skirt at all. It looked like one, however; it came down to her ankles, and was narrow enough and wide enough—but in reality it was a divided skirt, just like a riding habit.

"Test it, Miss Dunning," urged Mr. Ballard. "You said you might have to jump up on the ambulance. Try jumping with it now."

There was a leather horse with a saddle on it, where lady customers were accustomed to trying out their new riding suits. Emily jumped up on it. She jumped down. She swung her legs to the right and left. The suit was comfortable no matter what she did, with no danger of catching a heel in the skirt. The tailors assured her, moreover, that the divided skirt remained completely modest no matter what she did.

She was charmed with the clever way they hid pockets all over it. They were put in so expertly that they added no bulk.

If she could have afforded a suit costing a hundred dollars she could never have bought anything so right and so becoming to her. Ballard's were giving this to her as a gift and she was overwhelmed with gratitude.

The suit was the final touch needed to make her Christmas holidays of 1903 supremely happy. In a few days she would begin her internship at Gouverneur. Ben was well and putting on his normal weight, the twinkle back in his eyes. The family had all gathered together for the Christmas festivities and the house spilled over with their exuberance.

In that happy mood she read an ugly story in the newspapers and dismissed it from her mind as sheer gossip and rumor.

It was a story that there had been a petition circulated at Gouverneur, signed by all the doctors there and filed with the city government, protesting the appointment of Dr. Emily Dunning. The ugly story said that the doctors did not wish a woman on the staff because every six months the interns were moved up into different work, either doctoring or surgery, and eventually each became head of a division. Dr. Dunning, too, would be promoted in this way and the doctors were outraged that, when she became head, she could order about or dominate men doctors.

Also, the story went on, what would happen to the pleasant social hours of the men doctors? They were accustomed to lounging about in the social room in pajamas, and a woman doctor in the hospital would insist on decorum—on everything being stiff and proper.

Emily decided there was nothing to the story at all. She hadn't been officially told of any such petition. The newspapers were cooking it up because they had to have something to write about.

Gouverneur Hospital, 621 Water Street, faced with gray brick and standing square in front, had two round, curving wings reaching out to the East River in back. This was what she saw that first day in January of 1903 as the hired carriage dropped her and her suitcases off and she walked up the steps. She had been here before, to consult with Miss Stowers, the nursing superintendent, about her room, but that had been just a visit.

Now she was here to stay.

For a home, perhaps it left something to be desired, being functional rather than beautiful. It was severe and businesslike, and it smelled of iodine and carbolic acid. Just the same it was to be her home for two years and she sniffed the smells and looked with pleasure at the plain, painted walls.

Miss Stowers was as severe, as expressionless, as businesslike as the hospital itelf. She was there at the door to welcome Dr.

Dunning and to show her to her room. An orderly carried up the luggage.

Emily and Miss Stowers had already taken each other's measure and, while approving what they saw, each was reserving judgment about the other. Ben had said: "The superintendent is important. She is in charge of the living arrangements, the kitchen, the nurses. If she likes you, it will be a big help." Emily didn't think that Miss Stowers *liked* her, as yet, but she judged that the superintendent would be fair, impartial and not given to prejudices.

If that were so, it would be good. She might be able to influence the nurses. People had warned her that the nurses might resent taking orders from a woman doctor.

The nurses . . . the patients . . . her fellow doctors . . . all of them were still strangers to her on that day, as she unpacked and put her clothes away in her own room, washed and then changed to her white skirt and blouse. The nurses might not be such a problem; Emily had been the eldest and at times had had to tell her sisters, in no uncertain terms, what to do and what not to do.

About the patients she couldn't possibly guess. She would have to work hard for their respect; it wouldn't be easy, especially if they were males.

Her fellow doctors troubled her the least. Dr. John Rogers had once said to her, speaking of her working in a general hospital, that her men colleagues would "either love you or hate you." It seemed an exaggeration.

When she had finished unpacking and getting dressed, she went out into the corridors and found, as Miss Stowers had suggested, a Dr. Walter Parsons, a young man, who was making the rounds of the wards. She went with him and in this way became acquainted with the hospital—with the dispensary, the male wards, the female wards, the operating room, the waiting room, from which steps led down to the kitchen, where the nurses quarters were, as well as the staff dining room and the staff off-duty lounging room.

Dr. Parsons was busy and so they scarcely spoke, except for a question from her and a brief, businesslike answer from him. When it was over, she could not say she had formed any real opinion of him.

Back in her room she got ready for the early supper and at five o'clock made her way to the dining room. For some reason, she felt just a little shy and self-conscious. It was something of an ordeal to walk through the dining room, past the tables at one end where the nurses ate, to the table at the far end where the doctors sat in lordly splendor.

Then she saw Jerry Sheehan and immediately felt better. She remembered well the smiling, friendly Irishman, but she had forgotten that he would now be serving his second year at Gouverneur. Did he remember that if it hadn't been for her misfortune, for the fact that she had been refused her first place, he would not be here at all?

She smiled at him. He nodded. "Good evening, Dr. Dunning" was all he said and she felt a tiny shock. It was probably, she thought, the custom for the doctors at supper to be grave and distant and preoccupied, as they were now. Perhaps they wanted to set a good example before the nurses and not have them think medical men were frivolous.

The very young Dr. Batchelder did smile at her. They were both beginners here; this was the first day at Gouverneur for both of them and they would go through their whole two years together. Neither of them said much during the meal but she thought him very nice. They listened to the others talk of various patients, of treatments and the problem of a compound fracture of a leg which had just been admitted that day to the ward.

The food was good and plentiful and Emily was hungry. She had always been lucky that few things affected her appetite. From the way the doctors talked, she was going to need food to keep going during the long hours of work. Dr. Parsons complained to Dr. Sheehan that, unlike Bellevue and other city hospitals, Gouverneur had no meal served at midnight for the doctor on night duty.

As the meal was finishing, the man at her right did turn to her at last and ask: "Dr. Dunning, what is that contraption that was brought to your room yesterday? We've all been wondering."

"You didn't recognize it? It's a hospital bathtub, one of the large ones. I'm used to a cold bath every morning and since I knew there would be no private facilities for me, I tried to think of one I could keep in my room. One that wouldn't spill over or upset. Then I remembered these big hospital baths. Miss Stowers agreed that it could come into my room—although I admit it takes up a great deal of space. I've made arrangements with one of the maids to bring fresh water every morning and then to empty it when I'm dressed and gone."

"I hope you aren't going to make it a habit to demand extra work of the maids. They have plenty to do, as it is," said Walter Parsons.

Color flared into her face. "No. I shan't. There are very few problems of mine that can't be solved by the regular routine of the hospital. Miss Stowers was quite pleased with this solution to the question of baths."

It seemed to her they all exchanged glances, all except Dr. Batchelder, but then he was as much of a stranger there as she.

After dinner she was taken on a more extensive tour of the building, into every room and office. The work of each department was explained by the chief of staff, the senior physician in charge, and Emily realized that Gouverneur handled a great many patients for so few doctors. Her work would be cut out for her.

It was odd, she thought, that most of the doctors accompanied her and the senior physician and senior surgeon on that particular nightly tour. Certainly this was not usual.

Certainly these doctors had their own work to do, or else might have been relaxing off duty.

No matter—it was very kind and thoughtful of them to do this for her. Though they hadn't actually welcomed her with words or with even a smile, perhaps this was their way of showing they were solidly behind her and wanted her.

It was late and getting quite dark when they finished. They were in the hall outside one of the male wards when the senior surgeon turned to her, abruptly, and said:

"Dr. Dunning, you are on duty tonight. You will do the routine catheterizations in the male surgical ward."

She was so stunned she couldn't answer. She just looked at him and then, slowly, at the faces of all of the rest of the doctors in a circle around her. A mask had come off. This was not a welcome they had planned but a bit of cruelty. The job they had handed her, plotted for her, was the one they counted on to chase her out of the hospital and they had gathered to see the fun.

Catheterization was probably the most difficult of all jobs for a woman doctor to perform. Not difficult, technically, but from the standpoint of modesty.

There were male patients in that surgical ward who were unable to urinate. They had to be helped. Catheterization was the method required. Emily had known that someday she would probably have to do it, when she was more familiar with the patients and they had learned to trust and accept her, not as a woman, but as a doctor.

To give her this duty on her very first night was a nasty bit of plotting. They expected her to refuse, in shame and disgust.

She lifted her head. "Very well, Doctor," she said to the surgeon.

Someone in the circle gasped. That was not the answer they had expected to hear from her.

Emily turned to the orderly who was stationed by the male

surgical ward. She had been introduced to this doctor's helper earlier. "Martin," she said, "have you the catheters, the rubber gloves, and everything that we shall need, all in good condition?"

Don't think of anything except the job to be done. Don't think of the doctors—of the grinning faces of Walter Parsons and Jack Dowling and Dick Speed and Jerry Sheehan—especially not of that ungrateful Jerry Sheehan.

Don't think of anything but the job to be done. Once again, as had happened to her in the last examination, she felt that icy calm, that queer feeling that her person as a woman receded and the "doctor self" took over.

She quickly checked over the instruments and then motioned to Martin to precede her, while she followed him into the surgical ward. Behind her there was a momentary indecision; the doctors did not move; then someone shuffled his feet, someone coughed, the circle broke up and they drifted away. She felt their eyes on her back.

Martin opened the ward doors for her, and she could see that it was dimly lit and quiet inside the long oval room with the windows overlooking the East River. A tiny shaded light was just inside the door, otherwise only moonlight came in through the windows.

None of the patients spoke. They were dim shapes under their dark blankets. Their beds ran along the whole outside curve of the room. What would they do when they found that their doctor was a woman? Would they protest? Would they consider this an indignity?

Cold and clear, her mind asked the question without emotion. Whatever happened she would have to handle it or be beaten, run out of Gouverneur on her very first night.

"I want a portable screen we can carry from bed to bed, Martin," she said in a low tone. The patient in the nearest bed heard the feminine voice and raised his head from the pillow. "And a small table on wheels, to hold my instruments."

When the screen was brought she checked the list of those patients needing catheterization. Beds 1 and 3 and 7—on and on around the room. When the screen was properly placed, she stepped inside it and turned on the small bedside light, a dim one, just enough to see the hard, coarse, bearded face looking up at her. For just a second the calm almost deserted her. Gouverneur Hospital was in a district that included the Bowery, which was one of the toughest, roughest areas in the city. What would this man do? Insult her? Curse her? Refuse to let her treat him?

Don't think of anything but the job—she blocked out of her mind all the frightening possibilities and slipped on an impersonal, professional, masklike expression. She bent over the bed and worked gently and skilfully, but so fast that she was finished, had the blanket straightened and motioned to Martin to move table and screen to the next patient—before this one could say a word to her.

Nor did he say anything after she left. That was surprising. She worked around the room with lightning speed—though not for a second allowing her hands to be anything but gentle and kind—and no one in the whole room said a word. Yet they were watching her. She could feel eyes boring into her back.

She fought down the tension. If she became nervous she might hurt a patient. A sick man, hurt by a careless doctor, is an angry man, and it would take only one angry outburst for this whole room to break its unnatural silence and for the patients to start shouting abuse at her.

That was what the other doctors were counting on.

Suddenly Martin touched her arm. "That was the last one, Doc," he whispered.

She couldn't believe it. She doubted that catheterizations had ever been done so fast before. And still not a sound. Emily followed Martin as he rolled the little table toward the door, opened it and held it for her. Just before she went out she turned and looked back.

In the dim light she saw the face of her first patient. He was looking at her, thoughtfully and gratefully. On his coarse, rough face was a slight expression of wonderment—but none of the things she had feared: anger, mockery, abuse. He slid down under the covers and closed his eyes—and that was the nicest thing that could have happened to her. He was going to sleep. The doctor had come. Not a freak, not a woman out of place, just the doctor who had helped a sick man to sleep.

All over the room now there were those small peaceful, ordinary, natural noises of men turning over in bed to find a more comfortable place, sighing a little, beginning to snore, tugging at blankets or thumping pillows.

Tears started behind her eyelids and she felt a deep welling of affection for all these unknown men. The ordeal was over. They had given her a chance to prove herself and now they had accepted her. To them, ailing, sick, hurting men, she was just a doctor and they didn't care about her sex.

Nevertheless, she trembled as she went back to her own room. If she had been less skillful and quick and gentle, there might have been serious trouble. She blessed Dr. Sam Alexander, who had taught her urology and who had made her practice techniques over and over, anticipating that the time would come when she would have to do these jobs and do them even better than a man doctor.

She had no night duty, just this one job, so she could go to bed now and try to sleep.

As she undressed and brushed her long hair for a hundred strokes, she tried to reason out the plot. It seemed very likely to her now that there *had* been a petition signed by all these staff doctors to try to stop her from coming to Gouverneur. Obviously, it hadn't worked. So they had had to try other methods to drive her out.

This move tonight had been clever. First, there had been the possibility that she herself would refuse or protest against the task assigned. Second—and she had a hunch this was what they had counted on—the patients might have objected to her so strongly that she would have been forced to admit defeat and call upon another member of the staff.

Without doubt, if that had happened the doctors would have given the story to the newspapers the next day: RIOT AT GOUVERNEUR AGAINST MISS DUNNING. PATIENTS REFUSE WOMAN DOCTOR. These would have been the headlines. The staff at Gouverneur could then have applied to the city for her removal, for the good of the patients.

Oh, it was clever! But it hadn't worked.

She got into bed. The strain of the day and the evening was too much for her. She wanted to stay awake and think things out but instead she fell asleep almost immediately.

The next morning she felt her natural buoyancy come back. This was still her great, great adventure. If she said nothing and showed no offense or hurt or anger at the trick played on her last night, surely the staff would be good sports and accept her. Perhaps it would take a little time, a few weeks or a month; or perhaps last night would be their one try and now they would give up.

At breakfast time nothing was said about last night, although she felt the eyes of four of the doctors studying her, secretly, now and then.

Afterward, she and Dr. Batchelder were assigned their tasks for the next six months. They were subjuniors; they would alternate at handling the dispensary, three months on the medical service and three months handling the surgery— minor surgery, it would be. In addition, they must do the lowly jobs of making laboratory tests, taking case histories, and they would also be on call to administer the anesthesia when another doctor operated.

All on the staff were young doctors, serving their two years of internship. Every six months they moved up, both to a new job and to new prestige; every six months two interns left and two more were added to the staff.

At the top was the chief of staff, the house physician. The house surgeon was almost his equal, but it was the chief of staff who gave the orders for the day, made out the schedule for each and the assignments of night or day duty. Next came the senior physician and senior surgeon, junior physician and junior surgeon and, lowliest of all, the two subjuniors.

Because the staff members were young and relatively inexperienced, visiting surgeons and doctors, men of great prominence, came to Gouverneur from Bellevue, to operate or treat a very difficult case. They did not live at Gouverneur. They came on special call or to see a special patient or to check up, now and then, on the progress of all of the wards.

Whenever possible, a seriously ill or wounded patient was taken by ambulance to Bellevue or to some other hospital. Sometimes, however, to move a patient would have meant his death, and Gouverneur was specially set up to care for such emergencies, to operate immediately or to care for an illness which had flared into an acute stage.

The dispensary was a relatively easy job. Here came those with minor injuries or illnesses; men and women who could walk in, be sewn up or bandaged or receive a pill or be treated. Emily was glad she had done that special summer work with Dr. Gilley at the Center Street Dispensary. She had a good working knowledge. She knew, fairly well, the kinds of cuts and bruises and sprains she would have to handle.

There was a capable nurse who said, "Yes, Doctor" and "No, Doctor," as Emily questioned her about Gouverneur's procedures. She showed her where the case histories were kept and the various cupboards for jars, tubes, towels, bandages, splints and instruments.

"Yes, Doctor" and "No, Doctor" were about all she did

say, however. Her manner was neither friendly nor un-friendly, but very guarded. She acted as if she didn't quite know what to expect from Emily.

That was all right. All Emily expected was that both nurse and doctor work together for the patient. She would have to win the nurses' respect and once she did, and if they were willing to treat her as they would any medical man, she would be satisfied. She didn't demand that they be friends.

But if she could not win their respect, then it could be bad. There would always be times when the willingness of a nurse to put herself out, to work harder and longer in an urgent situation, could mean the difference between saving or losing the life of a patient. The relationship between doctor and nurse was one of mutual help. A quick nurse, an intelligent nurse, a thoughtful and considerate one, could assist to the extent that when a patient's life was saved she could feel they had done the job *together*.

It was too soon to tell what Emily would find. She knew that everything would have been much easier if one of the senior doctors had started her off this morning with an introduction to the nurse with a few pleasant words and a smile to bridge over the awkwardness.

The doctors practically ignored her. Several times one or the other of them would come to the door and look in. It hurt Emily to see the way they glanced around with quick, darting looks as if they were hoping to find her in trouble. Not one friendly gesture did they make, and she knew enough about hospitals and doctors to know that this wasn't usual. Ordinarily doctors went out of their way to help a new-comer to the staff.

Luckily, the morning went smoothly. Gouverneur Hospital took in an enormous number of cases through its dispensary. Emily was no sooner through with one patient who had a black eye, than the nurse brought in another with a sprained ankle. The benches outside were filled with people waiting their turn, men and women, and mothers with ailing children. They all displayed a lively curiosity in the "Lady Doctor," as Emily heard one describe her to the nurse. The women patients and the children took to her fairly quickly but the men were dubious.

They eyed her with mixed emotions as she first took down their histories: name, address, past illnesses, symptoms, etc. Then, reluctantly, they bared their chests so she could listen to a bronchial cough through the stethoscope, or parted their hair for her to examine a bad cut received during a tavern brawl, or opened their mouths to let her see their red, inflamed throats.

When she skilfully treated them, giving a pill or an injection, swabbing a throat or cleaning and bandaging a cut, their reactions were as varied as the men themselves. A few said, "Thanks, Doctor," a few more said breezily, "Okay, Doc," when she told them to come back for further treatments. Some seemed to resent the fact that she was so good at her job and that they had nothing to complain about and no sensational story to tell when they left.

One or two asked: "You going to be around here all the time?" One, honestly puzzled, demanded to know: "Are you a *real* doctor, lady?"

One man paid her a spontaneous and genuine tribute. "That's the ticket, Doctor," he said, after she had applied a soothing ointment to a rash on his neck and face. "It feels better already. You know your stuff all right."

A huge giant of a man, a longshoreman who worked on the water front, had come in with a dislocated shoulder. He was in considerable pain and Emily was tempted to call one of the other doctors for help. She knew what to do, but the man was so big and his shoulder so huge, so muscular, that she wasn't sure she could do it by herself.

One second's thought decided her. She didn't want to have to call for help from her unfriendly colleagues.

"I'm going to try to reduce the dislocation," she told the man. "If I can it will mean quick relief for you. But I will have to hurt you in doing it. I could call for another doctor and we'd give you an anesthetic and do it while you are asleep, if you'd prefer."

"That'll take time. Go ahead and try, Doc." he said.

The standard method was a complicated series of manipulations. Emily grasped his huge arm with her two slim hands; bending it at the elbow, then pressing it against his chest, she began rotating it. She was panting and gasping, while anguished sweat rolled off his forehead. With every ounce of strength she raised the arm high up in the air, rotating it just exactly as she had been taught to do in school—or as nearly exactly, since it had never been anticipated that a slim young woman would have to do this for a man weighing over two hundred pounds, whose arm and shoulder were the size of a tree trunk.

"Now!" she said, pulling back on the arm.

Snap! The head of the humerus went into place. The nurse on duty gave an audible gasp of surprise. The longshoreman's head went down on his chest in a gesture of complete abandonment to the great relief from pain. Emily sat down hard, trembling and aching all over from the exertion.

He raised his head. "And it's a hell of a foine doctor you are," he said, sincerely and fervently. He gave her a wide grin that split his Irish face. She smiled back weakly.

She was so proud of this case that she spent a little longer than necessary putting a bandage over his shoulder to keep firm those muscles that had already been hurt by the dislocation. And she watched him go out of the office with a feeling of real achievement.

Just from the kind of patients who drifted in, one by one, to the dispensary she began to get a slight picture of the very large area of New York which Gouverneur, in particular, serviced. It was the East Side and it included the water front, the Bowery, and a mixed-up general population of tenement dwellers, those from small factories, saloons and several prisons. Not a pretty district.

Even on that first day Emily saw that it was not all ugly in its nature. Poverty-stricken people came to the dispensary and humbled her with their courage in the face of pain, and their ability to smile and make a joke. When she spoke a little harshly about the necessity for cleanliness to a woman whose child had ringworm, Emily was horrified to find that the mother lived in a tenement flat that had no running water and no sanitary facilities. It was a marvel that the child was as clean as she was.

It would have been natural for a woman like Emily, brought up in such different surroundings and sheltered from the ugliness of life, to shrink from these people and show her discomfort and disdain. Though she did not know it then, the East Side was waiting for her to do just exactly that. The people who came to the dispensary were her judges; they were watching every gesture, every expression on her face, and listening to the tone of her voice.

But Emily respected courage. She appreciated the quality in human beings that made them laugh when by rights they should have cried. Even the toughs and the bullies prided themselves on being able to accept pain with no show of weakness, swaggering in their bravado. Emily understood. Life was terribly hard on all these people and she warmed to their swagger, since it was the only way they knew of fighting back.

She had walked into such a different world from the one she knew, but it fascinated her. She was quickly becoming so interested in her patients that she was only slightly hurt by the rudeness and the pinpricks of the doctors—and their attitudes no longer upset her as much as at first.

Once one of the doctors—she was too new to sort them all out by name—stopped by the doorway to listen as Emily was discussing a treatment with one of her cases:

". . . and if you will come back, without fail, every week, I'm sure we'll clear up this condition for you in a month. . . ."

The doctor interrupted. "In a month, Dr. Dunning? Hadn't you better make it quicker than that?"

The implication was clear. She would not last a month.

Emily's only reaction was to think to herself: *I'll be here a month—I'll be here two years. Don't think I won't!*

Once, too, she caught slightly flirtatious glances between one of the doctors and her nurse, and afterward the nurse looked at her a little apprehensively. She needn't have worried. Emily was not going to make trouble for her although, strictly speaking, the rules did not permit such flirtations.

The social relationships would be a delicate matter in the hospitals if she intruded upon them. Emily had decided months ago that some things would be none of her business. The nurses were young and pretty and the doctors were young and handsome; it was natural that they would be attracted to one another. Miss Stowers could be depended upon to watch out for the morals. A single word of criticism or reporting a nurse to the superintendent could put Emily in wrong from the start. Besides, she was in love with Ben and she could sympathize with the others.

That afternoon she was called upon to give a patient the anesthesia before an operation. Since it was not a difficult operation, the house surgeon would handle it, instead of calling in one of the prominent attending surgeons from outside.

Emily and Mary Baker, the nurse, were alone with the patient at first. The house surgeon was scrubbing his hands and getting ready in the adjoining room. Emily approached the patient who was lying quietly on the operating table and applied the customary small amount of chloroform.

Immediately the patient went wild. His arms flailed about;

he threw himself violently around on the table, almost sliding off. Emily had never heard of such a reaction and the
patient was getting wilder and more frenzied. Instinctively,
she called to the nurse: "Grab him!" and she herself poured
on a larger amount of chloroform than any textbook had
ever advised.

It worked. The patient subsided and went into the sleep
of anesthesia.

While she was standing over him and exchanging shocked
glances with the nurse, the house surgeon walked in. "Good,"
he said. "I see the junior surgeon must have explained this
case. The patient is a hard drinker and we've found that, with
a lot of alcohol in his system, he doesn't respond the way
normal people do. A little drives him crazy and makes him
uncontrollable; only a big dose of the anesthesia would put
him under."

It was on the tip of her tongue to tell him that no one
had warned her in advance. It was pure chance and her own
guesswork that had prompted her to do the right thing. She
didn't, because complaints and excuses on her very first day
would be interpreted as: "What do you expect from a woman?
Women always complain. They can't take it."

The escape had been a narrow one. If the house surgeon
had come in and found a patient threshing around the table
instead of being ready for an operation, or damaging himself
in his wildness, she would have been blamed. No excuse
would have helped her then.

Dinnertime went off under a surface of pleasantness, but
by now Emily had no illusions. Her four immediate superiors—Jerry Sheehan, Jack Dowling, Walter Parsons and
Dick Speed—most definitely did not want her at Gouverneur.
Just what they could do to drive her out, she didn't know.
She was a competent doctor so she was not so much worried
as she was depressed by it. They showed their contempt,

their unwillingness to accept her, in small, petty ways that hurt.

The house physician and house surgeon, though they must have been in the plot the night before, had evidently given up baiting her. This was their last six months at Gouverneur and their responsibility was to run the hospital with the least amount of friction; if Dr. Dunning could do her job, that would be to their advantage. Dr. Batchelder was neutral. Her difficulties lay with the other four.

7

They made her first six months at Gouverneur miserable, but she was to learn they had been nothing, just a prelude, to what was to come when the new six-month period began. At least the first six months had gone quickly; her dispensary patients had come very rapidly to respect and admire her and she had gained a great deal of confidence. She had no trouble with the nurses, even though she felt they were still watching and waiting and wondering about her.

It had been the steady pinprick of persecution—little things —which had robbed her of all pleasure in Gouverneur Hospital and made her dread coming back to it after her Sundays off.

She had told Ben only the lighter, more interesting side of her work. Ben was in love with her and if he knew that four strong young men were going out of their way to make her life disagreeable—he might have thought a thrashing would be the best way to handle them. Sometimes she longed to see that happen!

Her confidante was her mother. And Mama's advice was to keep silent, not to report the little acts of meanness, but to prove herself so good a doctor that she would eventually compel respect.

It was good advice but sometimes Emily wondered if it would work. She had found that patients were coming to the dispensary and asking for her, annoyed if the "Lady Doctor" wasn't there. Patients in the wards had circulated the story to new patients about Emily's first night at Gouverneur and how "swell" she had been, but none of this helped her with the doctors. In fact the effect was quite opposite.

Now the first six months were up and she realized with a jolt that the house surgeon and house physician were graduating. They had come to the point of respecting her and treating her decently, even clamping down a little on the others' persecution.

With their going, everyone moved up a step. Jack Dowling and Walter Parsons alternated as house surgeon and house physician; Jerry Sheehan and Dick Speed became seniors and she and Dr. Batchelder were juniors. Two new subjuniors came in: Drs. Taves and Colton. They quickly sized up the situation and, like Dr. Batchelder, decided to keep in the middle and not take sides.

So she was pitted against her four seniors. They had the power now. A hospital staff is something like the military: a junior does not rebel against a decision made by a senior and a junior does not refuse any assignment.

It was bitterly unfair, especially for Emily who was not one of those women who thought of men as natural enemies. Prejudice she fought, but not men. How could she, when she had such fine brothers and was in love with such a splendid man as Ben?

All that first day of her new promotion she watched and waited warily. She had worked through the morning and would go on ambulance duty in the early evening.

Dinnertime came and they opened fire at her. They had to maintain a certain pretense; they could not bluntly say to her: *Get out! We don't want you*—but they did everything else.

They knew she was worried about riding the ambulance. She was tired from the hours she had already put in and nervously and fearfully waiting for what would happen that night, so the four doctors talked of nothing but the dangers of the ambulance service.

"It takes tremendous physical strength to hang on when the ambulance is whipping along through the streets," said one. "Do you remember the time I almost fell off, Jerry?—"

"Sure, but that isn't the worst of it. An ambulance call can take you any place, into saloons or the most rotten dens of vice, or into the filthiest of alleys. That doctor's uniform is not going to protect you when a man is off his head with opium, or drunk, and a dark alley isn't the safest place for anyone to go at midnight. An ambulance driver has to pick up the victims of murder attempts and every possible crime."

Emily kept her eyes on her place and tried to eat. She would need that food. She was praying that they would stop talking about it; she was nervous enough, without all these lurid details and warnings.

Perhaps her impassive face fooled them and they thought this talk was not affecting her, but they were not discouraged. Dr. Emily Dunning still had to go out and ride that ambulance and they were positive that one night of it would finish her completely and that they would be rid of this female threat to their male domain.

Emily wondered and worried. This evening of June 30th was going to be a severe testing ground for her.

She was already dressed in her tailored uniform from Ballard's and she regarded it critically as she walked around in her room, waiting for the first call. No, no one would know it was a divided skirt. It looked quite like a real skirt and very nice, too.

At 5:30 P.M. a nurse tapped on her door. "Doctor Dunning? Ambulance call. A patient to be transferred from Beth Israel Hospital to Bellevue."

Emily went downstairs and was about to go out the front door when she saw the telephone. On impulse she hurriedly called her mother. "My first ride," she told her, trying to keep her voice light. "To Bellevue. Pray for me, dear."

"I will pray," came the strong and tender voice. "With all my heart."

Emily put down the receiver, feeling somehow a little more secure. She went out and crossed the street to where the stables were. The air was still hot for it had been a scorching day. It was still very light and people were outside, sitting on the steps of brownstone tenements or walking up and down, trying to get a breath of air.

From the stables came the sweet smell of hay and an odd mixture of harness polish, the wax polish used on the ambulance shafts to make them gleam, and, of course, the smell of horses. There was one small light already burning inside, though it wasn't necessary; she could see the stalls and the backs of the horses as they stomped restlessly. Here was the ambulance itself, its shafts pointing upward as if ready to go.

One of the drivers, already notified, was bringing out a horse with a big, long white head.

"I'm Dr. Dunning. We're to go to Beth Israel Hospital to pick up a patient and transfer him to Bellevue," she introduced herself to him, speaking also to two other drivers who sat comfortably around a cold iron stove as if from habit.

The first man held the horse with one hand and tipped his cap slightly to her with the other. "I'm Dick Bateman, Doctor. Be ready in a second."

"What is the horse's name?" she asked, admiring the slim, graceful, yet powerful, lines of the animal.

"This is Jim, Doctor. He's the best of all. You needn't be nervous with him."

"I expect I shall be a little nervous, just at first, but I shall get over it. And you aren't to bother or worry about me. You can't see me from your driver's seat, but if you worry about me in the back, then you won't be able to concentrate on your driving. I shall be all right."

Dick Bateman said nothing. Neither did the other two drivers. They looked at each other. One lit a pipe, the other studied his shoes as if they were of some importance.

The ambulance was backed out and Emily prepared to climb up onto her perch at the back. It looked difficult and she hesitated a moment. Suddenly Dick Bateman was at her side and he was saying, "Doc, I'd like to show you a trick or two, how to get on the bus, if you want me to."

She flashed him a grateful look that was from the bottom of her heart.

"Look," he explained, showing her how to step up in one motion, seat herself, and then swing her skirt and her feet up in one flip over the tailboard, whirl herself around in almost the same motion so that she was facing forward, reach with both hands for the leather straps—and there she was. It was neat, it was quick—and it was a safe method.

She practiced it twice and then got the hang of it. Bateman left her sitting there, then he climbed up onto his own seat in front, backed the ambulance out into the street and they were off.

It gave her a queer thrill. This was the "bus"—the ambulance which was the mercy wagon for so many people in New York. She knew its history. There had been no ambulances in New York until after the Civil War. A Bellevue doctor named Dr. Edward Dalton had used a light wagon on the battlefield and had come back to New York afterward, determined to introduce that wagon into regular hospital practice.

He had argued with the authorities: "Look," he had said, "no matter how fine our service is, people die before they can reach the hospital. They have to walk or be carried, the seriously ill and poor have to find some kind of vehicle they can ride in." He told them about a badly injured man who had been taken into the nearest house where he lay bleeding to death. Kind Samaritans had gone to the nearest man who had a horse and wagon, but that horse had worked all day and was tired. Another horse had a stone in its shoe. It was three o'clock in the morning before a horse and wagon could be found; the man died from the terrible jolting of the cart and the long delay before he reached Bellevue.

Dr. Dalton had designed the ambulance which, except for slight changes, was still in use in Emily Dunning's time. The center part was a wooden structure, closed in, long enough and wide enough for a patient to lie down in and for the doctor to move by the stretcher side if necessary. In it, too, were the blankets, the padding, strips of various lengths with buckles to be used for restraining violent patients; there were also bandages, tourniquets, sponges, and a flask of brandy for a stimulant.

In front, open to the weather, sat the driver. In the back, also in the open, sat the doctor on a slippery seat that was more nearly a ledge than a seat.

Here Emily perched as the ambulance trotted down the streets toward Beth Israel Hospital. Some emergencies demanded every bit of speed, but this one was not that drastic. Jim, the horse, could go at a trot and Emily was able to look about her, not just concentrate on hanging on for dear life.

What a wonderful thing to be free! She was out of the hospital, away from her tormenters and on her own. There was the glorious sensation of riding along and not having to do anything for the moment but catch the little breeze in her face and look about her, with fascination, at this district of the East Side.

A poor district it was, but at the same time so rich in variety—warehouses, shops, tenement buildings with iron fire escapes straggling down into dark alleys, politicians' hangouts, saloons and taverns. Wherever there was a small strip of park, it was filled with shouting, active children. People were everywhere; the population of the East Side, crowded into these tenements, was unbelievable.

The people on the sidewalks and on the front steps caught sight of Emily. They edged close to the curb and stared. She felt like an exhibit in a zoo but she didn't care; the ambulance "bus" clipped on at a fast rate and she was exhilarated.

At Beth Israel Hospital the attendant at first refused to believe that Emily was a doctor and she had the authority to take the patient away. However, there was the signed pass; there she was in her uniform cap with Gouverneur Hospital on it, and outside the ambulance waited. The patient was brought down on the stretcher and placed in the ambulance.

Getting to Bellevue meant retracing their former route and the word had spread all over the East Side. Now there were crowds lining the sidewalks to watch the phenomenon of a woman riding the ambulance. Here was a game! The people on the streets were bored, tired, hot and listless, wanting some excitement in their lives, and this was it. They laughed. They cheered, mockingly. Small boys ran alongside the ambulance wheels yelling, "Get a man, get a man!"

The word had spread even as far as Bellevue, which was not surprising since the day before the newspapers had made much of the fact that Emily would ride an ambulance for the first time the following day.

When they arrived at the gates of Bellevue Hospital there was a crowd around it, waiting, avidly curious. Emily's exhilaration was all gone by now and such crowds and such open, naked curiosity—partly hostile, partly jeering—made her feel horrible. She wished she could run away and hide. Then suddenly she caught sight of a lovely, smiling and proud face in that crowd and her heart lifted to meet that smile.

Mama had come. She was standing there. The ambulance and Emily went through the gates of Bellevue with banners flying. Mama's smile had said *"Courage!"*

The patient was safely taken into the receiving room at Bellevue. Going back, Dick Bateman had to flourish his long whip at times to make the crowds back off the streets. The little boys were in full cry behind, yelling, "Get a man, get a man!"

Yet when the ambulance drove into the hospital driveway at the back of Gouverneur to let Emily off, she was laughing. The driver's face showed his relief when he saw her laughter and he grinned too. She stood by his seat for a second before going in. "Thank you again for showing me how to get up on the 'bus.' Will you be on duty with me all through the night?"

"Yes, Doc. And don't let those kids and the crowds bother you, Doc."

The next call came an hour later. By that time there were fewer people on the streets and almost no small boys to yell at her. The ride went off without an incident except that the "bus" was going so fast this time that Emily's heart was in her mouth. She had no time to think of people or whether they were staring at her or pointing at her or jeering at her. All she could do was hang on for dear life, very frightened.

Most of the calls for the ambulance came from policemen. The one who made this particular call was waiting for her at one of the docks at the water front. A sailor had fallen into the deep hold of his ship and been injured. He would be her patient.

The policeman had been trained not to show emotion, but his shock at seeing a woman doctor was almost too much for him. "Didn't they explain to you, Miss—I mean, Doctor—that you'd have to go on board ship and down into the hold? You can't do it. I'll have to call Gouverneur and have them send a man doctor."

If he did that she was finished! One refusal by a policeman or a patient or a nurse to work with her would be enough to force her resignation.

"You go ahead, Officer, and I'll follow. If I have to climb down into a ship's hold, I'll climb down." Seeing that he was not convinced, she smiled and added, "I had three brothers and I could climb up and down our pear tree at home just as easily as they could."

He hesitated for a moment, then he signaled to another policeman to come along, too. They went up the gangplank and onto the ship.

There were no steps going down to the hold, only a rope ladder which swung about, carelessly, at every touch. Before Emily had a chance to be afraid, the first policeman was already going hand in hand down the rope; she followed; the other policeman came right after.

Emily thought, With all our weight on this ladder it will surely break! That thought gave way to another, to an understanding of *why*. The policemen were being especially considerate so that whether she looked up or down she would not see dizzying emptiness; she would see only their broad-shouldered blue uniforms. For this she was grateful.

The sailor had fractured some of the bones in his feet and Emily put them into splints, wrapping them very carefully so that when he was carried up he would feel the least possible pain.

Once again she climbed the rope ladder with the two policemen solidly there, ready to catch her, keeping her from being aware of how far down that hold was and how dangerous that rope ladder.

As the sailor was put into the ambulance she thanked her two blue-coated protectors. Their faces were impassive but the eyes of one showed surprise. "It's you we should thank, Doctor. It makes our jobs easier if we work with doctors who aren't afraid of a bit of danger."

All that night she went back and forth on the ambulance. In between calls the senior surgeon on duty at Gouverneur allowed her no rest; she worked in the accident ward on the very patients she had brought in. And at breakfast time she was told she would continue on the ambulance all that day, too.

She had had no sleep. She was tired, but doggedly she went on. Her driver that day was Tom White and he showed, in small, unobtrusive ways, the same kindnesses that Dick Bateman had. On one of her calls she had to examine an unconscious man. She had to decide, on the spot, whether or not the man was dead drunk, ill or hurt. If he was drunk, then the ambulance would take him to the station to sober up.

It was extremely difficult to make such an on-the-spot diagnosis, particularly with the crowd staring at her, and with newspaper reporters clustering around, wanting a story from her. It was then that Tom stepped in. As they both bent over the unconscious man he whispered, "He's all right, take him to the police station."

From years of driving an ambulance, watching both doctors and drunks, Tom had developed a sixth sense and could tell instinctively if a man was sick or drunk.

Emily was grateful for the help. She knew that the four doctors back at Gouverneur were watching every move she made, expecting with each call to hear that she couldn't take it any longer, that the East Side had refused to have a woman in their district, or that she had made a mistake. She could just hear the caustic remark if she brought in a drunk: "Really, Doctor, don't you know when a man has had a drop too much? This is a hospital, not a sobering-up police station."

Whatever she did that day was noticed and written up by the newspaper men. They followed her everywhere she went. They besieged her for stories, but even if she had wanted to give them one—and she didn't—the Medical Board had instructed her never to talk to reporters.

So, late in the afternoon, exhausted and badgered by them, after she and Tom White had safely delivered a patient to

Bellevue, she sought refuge for a few moments in the ambulance stable. No one knew she was there and it was peaceful and quiet. The horses stood, relaxed, in their stalls and moved only to twitch a tail at a fly or to shift positions with a thump of hoofs. Tom made little encouraging sounds as he unhitched big Babe who was playful and wanted to skirmish a little instead of going placidly into his stall.

To Tom and the other drivers, the horses were personalities. "This one," he indicated Babe, "is so good-natured you can do anything with him. He isn't as smart as Jim—Jim's the best. He'll race his heart out for you and he's intelligent. Sometimes he's clumsy, but Babe's such a friendly sort of cuss."

Emily sat back in one of the padded chairs around the stove, which was not in use during those hot days. It was so nice to sit there and have a man talk to her without having to worry about what trick he was thinking up.

"And the other?—the big bay with the white feet?" she asked.

"That's Stockings. He's almost as smart as Jim. And courage? Why, that horse doesn't know the meaning of fear or quit." He was rubbing Babe down vigorously, because the horse had been ridden hard. "Don, that big gray over there, is as sour as they come. He doesn't like us; he doesn't like the ambulance; he doesn't like anything. But give him a little touch of the whip and Don can really run."

A man with a hard, round hat came in the stable door, spoke to Tom White, looked at Emily and walked out. Two small boys, sucking bits of ice which they had stolen off the bottom of the ice truck, wandered in and sat in a corner as if they were accustomed to being there. They had eyes for the horses, not for Emily, though one smiled shyly when she did.

"People do drop in here," the driver explained. "Not that it's a hangout, you understand, Doc. But there's always men visiting their wives, say, over in the hospital. Or politicans like that man who looked in here, who come to visit some ward worker who might be laid up in an accident at Gouverneur and—well, they stop in here and say a few words. Especially on a cold night, when the stove's going and it's warm in here, men and kids come in."

"Of course." She wasn't sure why he was telling her this. Maybe just to make conversation? Anyway, it was time she got back to the hospital and to work. She straightened up and Tom White came over to her, wiping his hands on a rubbing cloth.

"What I mean to say is, we hear a lot of the talk that goes around. Remember that big longshoreman came into the dispensary and you fixed up his dislocated shoulder? Well, he was in here bragging about what a fine doctor you are— and if anybody said anything against you, he was going to crack 'em down with his fist." He threw the rag into its proper corner. "Well, after today there's some others feel the same way about you, Doc."

She walked back to the hospital feeling as if she wanted to cry just a little. Her longshoreman had passed the word; the drivers had decided to give her a chance; and now Tom White was saying that she had proved herself to them and they were on her side.

Rags, the stable dog, had followed her to the hospital. She bent down and patted him on the head and told him to run back to the driver. The dog had taken to her right away; he was a friendly little mutt who considered himself just as much a part of the ambulance service as doctors or horses or drivers, and each time they went out he raced behind.

As soon as her shift for the day was over she fell into bed, after she had undressed, and went to sleep instantly.

It seemed to her only minutes before there was a rap on her door. "Dr. Dunning. You are on duty in surgery." Emily looked at the bedside clock, unbelieving. She had slept only four hours and she had been on duty before that for nearly twenty-four straight hours. This couldn't be true. It was more than just unfair.

She lay for a second with her eyes closed. The tactics of wearing her down physically so that she could no longer stand it, or would make a serious mistake because her mind was groggy, was suddenly a very serious thing to her.

The tactics could work. The human body could stand only so much and no more. It was entirely possible that she would break down under the combined physical strain and the emotional pressure on her. If she only weren't standing so alone at Gouverneur!

There was cold water in the basin and she slapped it vigorously over her face and neck and arms. It revived her and she finished dressing and went down to surgery, where she assisted Dr. Parsons for two hours. He was unnecessarily abrupt and caustic with her, finding fault when there was really none to find.

Back she went to bed and then up for early breakfast, making herself feel awake and alert only by the sheer force of her will.

Her day then was typical of what she could expect. At 9:20 A.M. she was sent to transfer two adults and two children to Bellevue. Out on the "bus" to a ship where a man with tuberculosis collapsed just as she arrived, and she had terrible moments when giving him stimulation to revive him. Next, she and Murray—Tom Murray, called Murray to distinguish him from the other Tom—took the ambulance to the better-equipped Bellevue stables to have the tires inspected, while Emily went to the drug room to collect drugs for Gouverneur, then to the storeroom to get a barrel of flour, tin cups and a package already wrapped. Back at the dispensary at 11:10, with twenty-four cases piled up there and waiting. Though this was the subjunior's job she must pitch in and help.

All afternoon was spent at the dispensary. At four she was

off and could go get cleaned up and count on a pleasant dinner and early bed.

But no. She was ordered to take first call on the ambulance after dinner. And after that to relieve Dr. Taves in the operating room. There was a difficult obstetrical case and the baby had been stillborn. She arrived in the operating room to find Dr. Dowling there but he left her in charge.

The woman on the bed was slowly regaining consciousness and Emily dreaded the moment when she would have to tell her that her child had not been born alive. Soon, however, there was a graver matter; the woman's pulse was growing weaker. Emily reported this to Dr. Dowling, who ordered stimulation. It did not help. When Dr. Sheehan came on duty Emily reported it to him. He ordered medication. On her own, Emily began Crede's massage, the only desperate hope left. The woman hemorrhaged; a little blood showed.

For an hour she and the nurse kept up the massage but it was no use. The nurse touched Emily on the arm and they looked down at the dead face of the woman.

It was now late in the evening. With the horror of the death upon her, Emily sent word to Dr. Sheehan and waited, but he did not come, and she had to take the responsibility herself of pronouncing the patient dead and of admitting the grief-stricken father to the bedside.

When she finally crept up to bed she was drained of all energy, from the long day of nine in the morning until after ten at night and the sadness of death and grief. Her sleep was troubled and she woke feeling anything but fresh. Even the cold bath barely helped.

That afternoon, the visiting surgeon Dr. Francis Huber spoke to her about the dead woman. In telling the whole story, Emily mentioned that there had been a hemorrhage, that the woman had lost blood.

A few minutes later Dr. Parsons met her. "What is this

you've been telling Dr. Huber—that the woman hemorrhaged? She did not!"

Emily realized then that Dr. Huber was upset and felt that
in the case of hemorrhage the senior surgeon should have
been there; that Parsons had been negligent.

Dr. Parsons convinced Dr. Huber that there had been no
hemorrhage.

That night at dinner, after she had worked hard on ambulance call all day, Emily was subjected to an unmerciful tor-
rent of scorn and mocking jests from the four doctors. "Our
lady doctor doesn't know a hemorrhage when she sees it,"
said one. And another: "Be careful, Dr. Dunning, a drop of
blood evidently scares you until you think it is a hemorrhage."

She let them talk on. Be silent, her mother had advised,
and now it was good advice, because if she had ever opened
her mouth now she could not have trusted herself to stop.
She would have said things . . . !

So the summer went on, with every day demanding the
last ounce of courage and strength and self-control she
possessed. Sometimes, when she had had a full day's duty
and could sleep at night she would go into her own room and
hear, from the doctor's quarters, the noise of laughter and
gaiety. Those off duty were having a party. Emily had never
been lonely before in her life; it seemed hard that, in addition to everything else, she should have to be so cut off from
this social life.

She couldn't have joined, of course, even if they had invited her. They ordered up beer from the saloon across the
street and, while Emily had not the slightest objection to their
drinking beer, she had decided before she came that every
action of hers must be a careful one. The newspapers would
not leave her alone and she could see the headlines: WOMAN
DOCTOR CAROUSES; BEER PARTIES AT GOUVERNEUR WITH FE-
MALE COMPANIONSHIP. No, it wouldn't do.

There was a common lounge which she used as well as the men. This could have been her social room if the others had been sociable toward her.

Was all this—the work, the loneliness, the fear of making mistakes, the persecution and the torment—worth her sacrifice for them? Yes. Definitely, yes. She knew that. At Gouverneur she was learning things in her profession she could never have hoped to learn elsewhere. She had had to handle every kind of medical and surgical case, in almost every kind of situation. When she left, she would be a very experienced doctor, indeed.

But still, if it hadn't been for her days off which she could spend with her family and Ben, and if it hadn't been for the freedom she felt on the ambulance, away from the hospital, she wasn't sure she could have endured. Her days off were like walking from gloom into sunshine or from prison into freedom. Her mother and Amy petted her and indulged her to make up for the bruising her spirit was taking the rest of the six days of the week. Harry was on vacation from Cornell, but working during the summer, and he did everything he could to make her laugh, worrying because that natural, spontaneous, contagious laugh of Emily's was a bit strained now.

Margaret, with her sense of style, insisted on arranging and rearranging Emily's hair, to keep up her morale and make her realize that she was still a lovely and attractive young woman. Young Ned worshiped her and Will advised her.

Ben more than made up for what those four young men at the hospital were doing to her. Her starved affections, her rigid self-control, the feeling that she walked a tightrope at Gouverneur, vanished under the warmth of Ben's love. In his eyes she saw another Emily—attractive, desirable, admirable. With him she was feminine and perfectly natural.

Doctors both, they could help each other. By this time Ben knew something of what she was undergoing. He was angry but he knew the code of hospitals and reluctantly agreed that Mrs. Dunning's advice was the only one possible: Keep silent, don't complain, see it through.

"It won't be forever," Ben consoled her. "Parsons and Dowling will be finished in January and Sheehan and Speed will complete their internship next July. It's a whole year. Do you think you can hold out that long?"

"If I do, it will be because of the ambulance," she told him. "Remember how timid I was about horses? I still am, a little. I am sometimes frankly terrified when the drivers have to gallop through the streets on an emergency. I can't see where we are going, sitting back where I am, and I can't anticipate when we will swing around a corner. I have to brace myself—and even then I go sliding back and forth on that little seat and sometimes I just save myself from falling off the back." She smiled and threw back her head. "But, oh, that wonderful feeling of being free and on my own when I ride the 'bus'!"

"What about the people in the district—in the East Side? Do they give you any trouble?"

She frowned. "Not really. I seem to feel there is a little change in attitude, but it is too soon to tell. Some of the policemen actually are glad to see me arrive. And the ambulance drivers—Ben, no one could ask for better champions. They are like the knights of old; almost too chivalrous."

"Thank God for that!" said Ben fervently.

"Let me tell you." It was such a relief to be able to talk to him about all this. "The other day we had to go into a Bowery saloon, where there had been a fight. We got the injured man into the ambulance all right; then I had to go back and question the sailor who had been mixed up in it. He was able to talk but he was extremely drunk. All of his drunken fury was turned on me, a meddling woman, and then he began to say some pretty shocking things to me. We were standing up against the bar when suddenly I saw a big, clenched fist slam down on the bar counter between me and the sailor. It was Murray, the driver. One look at that fist and one look at Murray and the sailor turned into a very polite and cooperative man."

"That was all right," she continued. "I was very grateful. But Dick Bateman carried it a bit too far. We had to pick up a dentist who was raving, and much too happily drunk and take him to the police station. On the way there he let loose such a continuous stream of profanity and obscenities against me and against the straps with which we had to bind him that he could be heard up front by the driver as well as by me. I couldn't stand it any longer so I took a pad of gauze and slapped it over his mouth, fastening it down with adhesive tape. It was drastic but it gagged him. Well, I found out days later, from the other drivers, that Dick had waited until the dentist was released, sober, by the police, then went to his home and thrashed him for abusing me."

8

The main reason why Ben had to keep his anger in check was the danger of a story reaching the newspapers. Not for a moment did the interest of the reporters in Emily slacken; they hung around the hospital and around her, trying to get a story that would be sensational.

They went so far as to frame a stunt. A reporter planned to jump overboard from one of the wharves, making sure that a policeman would see him; the call would go to Gouverneur for an ambulance to save the poor man from overexposure, Emily would rush forth—and the other reporters who were in on the gag, would have a fine joke to report. They could almost see the headline:

LADY DOC BELIEVES IN FAKE SUICIDE

Everything went exactly as they had planned except for one detail. For once—since even senior doctors until they became head physician or head surgeon also answered ambulance calls at times—it was not Emily but Dick Speed who rushed with the ambulance to the wharf.

The hoax was discovered and Dick Speed came to dinner immediately afterward, glaring daggers at Emily who had been the innocent cause of his unnecessary trip.

The heat never let up all that summer and on into fall. Emily was swamped by calls of people dropping on the sidewalks from heat prostration. After rescuing them, she had to return to the hospital wards where the smells of disease and rotting sores and wounds hung like a suffocating blanket in the still, warm air. She was overly tired from the too-long hours and interrupted sleep. But the work went on.

And the persecution continued.

Mealtimes had come to have a great importance in her life. She was constantly hungry and she knew that if her strength was not to fail then she must eat, no matter how much the four of them plagued her.

"Dr. Dunning," said Dick Speed, just as she was sitting down to lunch, "there is an emergency case waiting for you in the treatment room. Please go down and see her immediately."

She had to go. Downstairs she found that Dick Speed had previously examined the woman and done a preliminary opening of a dressing on a varicose ulcer. When she lifted it to see, she found it crawling with maggots! The ulcer was alive with them. For a moment Emily was completely nauseated; she wanted to run somewhere and vomit. Then she realized that that was his intention. He knew what the ulcer looked like. He knew it could have waited until after lunch or he could have attended to it before, himself.

I'll have my lunch, she thought. *I need it. I'm no good to this patient or any other if I faint from weakness.*

She replaced the dressing, informed the patient that she would return shortly, washed her hands thoroughly and went upstairs and finished her lunch with as good an appetite as possible.

Yet she was not always absolutely successful in her iron control. One day she had made the rounds of the wards with Dr. Sheehan. There was one patient who was having serious chills. After the rounds, Dr. Sheehan left to go play tennis and she was in charge of that ward. The case worried her. Tests had been made for malaria and for typhoid but they had proven negative. Emily knew that further tests should be made. She didn't know what to do; Dr. Sheehan was her superior and he had not ordered these tests. It was a serious matter for her to take on responsibility when she was only standing in for him while he played tennis.

At three o'clock Jerry Sheehan returned in a hurry because the great Dr. John F. Erdman, the visiting surgeon, was due. There was no time for Emily to speak privately to Sheehan about the patient with the chills; they went immediately into the operating room and were there with Dr. Erdman for some time. Afterward, Dr. Erdman wanted to visit the ward to check on another patient.

As he passed the bed, he saw the chills and the shaking, and his quick eye suggested that there might be something more serious. "There must be pus there somewhere," he said, pausing. The three of them discussed this particular patient and the fact that the malaria and typhoid tests had failed. Emily added that the patient was having two chills a day and she suggested that perhaps it would be in order to make a leucocyte test.

Dr. Jerry Sheehan concealed his fury as long as Erdman was there but at dinner time that night he gave Emily a brutal tongue-lashing. She could only say: "Dr. Sheehan, this is no time and place for such criticism, not with the nurses listening."

"What place could be better than the dinner table to call down an intern for stupid blundering," he said loudly. But it was not a blunder; it was the fact that she had shown up his own negligence that was making him so angry that he lost all discretion. "What were you trying to do, Dr. Dunning, curry favor with Erdman? Make him think you were so bright? Try to insinuate that the rest of us know nothing and you know everything? A leucocyte count! If I had thought such a thing was necessary, don't you suppose I would have ordered it? This hospital has no place for prima donnas or publicity seekers."

She broke down. She had protested in the only way she could; she was helpless to stop him because he was her senior. To her horror, the tears came and her whole body was wrenched with deep sobs. But she would not stop eating— she had to have that food or she would never get through the rest of the day.

Sobbing uncontrollably, she ate on, cutting her meat into the smallest of pieces and forcing herself to choke them down. After a while even Dr. Sheehan couldn't stand to see such a spectacle and he hurriedly left the table.

Her eyes were swimming with tears so that she could hardly see what she was eating, but she raised them once and caught a sympathetic and understanding glance from young Dr. Colton, one of the newest members of the staff.

The new doctors could not help her. They were caught between two fires and, like Dr. Batchelder, they settled it by treating her as well as they possibly could—yet not declaring themselves on her side. After all, they, too, were juniors and, being men, they shared the men's quarters and the men's social evenings.

The persecution not only hurt Emily; it also hurt the four doctors who planned it. No doubt they were not alone. Other doctors in other hospitals must have appealed to them: do something about Emily Dunning! If she sticks it out at Gouverneur and reaches the point where she becomes house surgeon and then chief of staff, it will open all the doors. We'll be having those females at our hospitals, Heaven forbid.

So it was up to Walter Parsons and Dick Speed and Jack Dowling and Jerry Sheehan to stop this terrible menace. They looked upon what they were doing as a principle, even if they must be unprincipled about it. It was a crusade and they were self-righteous, convinced that women didn't belong in the general hospitals.

The hurt it did them was serious. Basically, they were all decent young men. They were fine doctors, with skill and technique and a genuine feeling for their patients. But to get at Dr. Dunning meant they had to be ruthless even to the point, sometimes, of endangering a patient in order to endanger her. If they had stopped to realize—but they didn't.

One day Dr. Dowling and she were examining a woman about to give birth to a child. If the delivery was not to be immediate, then the best place for her was at Bellevue Hospital. Dr. Dowling ordered that Emily take the patient there in an ambulance. From all of her experience, in working with Dr. Jacobi, Emily was sure the birth would be soon. She protested that it was too dangerous to remove the woman now.

Perhaps if Emily had not protested, Dr. Dowling would have made a more cautious judgment, but that protest was all he had to hear. If Dr. Dunning said the woman should remain, then the woman must go.

The ambulance, carrying the woman, raced as driver and horse had seldom done—not even for a fire—and Emily prayed that the birth would be delayed until she could get the patient safely into a hospital bed in Bellevue. It was not to be. The child was born just as Emily was helping the woman into the Receiving Room.

Only the instinct of a doctor, the quick reaction of Emily's muscles, saved them from a horrible tragedy that could almost be called murder.

For babies, Emily would throw away her caution. Back at Gouverneur Hospital she marched into the ward where Dr. Dowling was and told him, strong and straight, just what had happened and what his responsibility would have been if the baby hadn't been caught in time. "Dr. Dowling," she told him, "you know as I know that this hospital is for just such emergency cases as this, for patients who cannot be moved with safety."

He was taken aback both by her unprecedented action in standing up to him and by the enormity of what he had done. Shock was in his face but Emily drove the point home:

"Don't you ever dare to ask me to take a case like this again, for I shall flatly refuse to do so."

Summer brought with it short vacations for the staff and that meant doubling up in work. Summer also brought temptations for the senior members of the staff to relax a little, get a cool breath of air boating on the river or playing tennis in the mornings. In one sense, they were entitled to it. As senior members, their responsibilities on duty were very heavy and so they must relax when they could.

Actually, the hardships fell mainly on Emily. A man in her place, associating in the evenings with the four senior doctors, might have good-humoredly protested, "Look—I can't carry all this extra work. You're taking too much time off." And his seniors, with as much good humor, would have recognized they were carrying a privilege too far.

Emily could not protest, not against too much work. It was too delicate a question, since the principal objection to her was that a woman couldn't stand up under the work of Gouverneur. No, she had to stretch a single day out to twenty-six hours and keep quiet.

When Dr. Parsons, house surgeon, was on vacation, Dr. Sheehan took over as acting house surgeon and he also took advantage of his position by being away a good deal of the time. Emily not only had her own work to do but often had to pinch-hit as house surgeon. On one such very trying day, Dr. Sheehan returned to the hospital around seven. He turned over one of his cases to her, told her she would have to be on active duty on Sunday, her day off, then out he went to be gone for the rest of the evening, leaving Emily to act as house surgeon.

She had just a few hours sleep, then she was back on duty

all day Sunday. That Sunday evening she was on first call to
ride the ambulance!

But, unknown to Emily, what she was doing and what
was being done to her was not going entirely unnoticed. In
a hospital, word travels. People—patients, nurses and visiting
doctors—had eyes and ears to see what was going on. Not
everything was seen and not all at once, but slowly, slowly,
things were changing.

On that same day while Dr. Sheehan was away he had left
word for her to do some dressings. There just wasn't time
for them, and for a moment there was an expression of hopeless despair on Emily's face as Miss Stowers relayed the
message to her.

With no inflection in her own voice, and careful not to let
the slightest shade of feeling come through, Miss Stowers
quietly said, "I shouldn't think, Dr. Dunning, that you would
feel under any obligation to do them."

The superintendent in her own quiet way, was a powerful
figure in the hospital. Emily took her cue and simply did
nothing whatever about the dressings.

A few weeks later, with the pressure keeping her working
at nerve-racking speed, she had a few more very bad days.
In the morning she was on the ambulance, on her way to the
ghastly scene of a murder, and had to take the victim back
to Gouverneur. Then she was again on the ambulance, bringing in a wounded man who had been run over. Trips to
Bellevue and back; then in the wards for a while and then off
to police court to testify about the condition of a man who
was suing for injuries in a disability case. These were only
the highlights of her day. In between she acted as house surgeon in Dr. Sheehan's absence.

The next morning Dr. Sheehan made an appearance and
then went out, returning for lunch. Emily went about her
own work, not knowing that he had gone out again in the
afternoon.

Suddenly she was summoned by the hospital secretary, very shaken and upset: "Please, Dr. Dunning—Dr. Erdman is coming here and he wants the operating room made ready and an ambulance sent for a patient."

"Why don't you notify Dr. Sheehan?" Emily asked.

"I can't," the secretary's voice dropped to a whisper. "He's out again."

Emily moved about at lightning speed. She got her associate Dr. Batchelder to go out with the ambulance, pick up Dr. Erdman's patient and bring him to the operating room. She took charge in there, getting table and instruments, nurses and orderlies ready.

When Dr. Erdman arrived, his quick eyes noted everything. Perhaps they had noticed a good deal before because he said to her, "Dr. Dunning, you are house surgeon until Dr. Parsons gets back. I have temporarily suspended Dr. Sheehan."

Not until the operation was over and the visiting surgeon had departed did Emily realize what he had said and what that meant. It would only be a few days before Walter Parsons returned, but until that time she—*she!*—was acting house surgeon and not Jerry Sheehan.

It would have been a splendid time for revenge but she was too wise to take it. As house surgeon for a few days, Dr. Sheehan was under her orders as was every other doctor working on surgery. She was on a par with the chief of staff, the house physician. She felt tremendously proud that Dr. Erdman had singled her out in this way but she also knew that Dr. Sheehan would dislike her all the more for it. And once Dr. Parsons returned, everything would go back to its old status and she would again be the prey of her tormentors.

The prey, yes, but not quite as helpless as before, she thought. Dr. Erdman's recognition of her as a capable doctor and as an individual gave her the courage to say "no" once in a while. So when Dr. Parsons was back again, and they started to pile the work on her, she learned politely to refuse.

She started out by being polite, but sometimes she just dug her heels in and bluntly refused.

One of her jobs when she was junior surgeon, was to see that all instruments used in operations were cleaned afterward, sterilized and put away. She looked after this faithfully. One time, however, she went off ambulance duty and surgical room duty at five o'clock, which she was supposed to. Dr. Parsons was still operating and the schedule called for further use of the operating room. She could not possibly go in to look after the used instruments. This was done only when the room was empty.

So at five o'clock, exhausted, she went to her room and contemplated the rare, blissful pleasure of an early supper, a few minutes to attend to her hair and her clothes, and then immediately into bed. It was incredible how rarely she had slept there a whole night through. There was no reason to believe that on this night there might not be an emergency call for her on the ambulance. But all in time. At seven she was in bed, reading.

There was a knock on her door. She wrapped a dressing gown around her and went to answer it. There was Walter Parsons, thunder like a cloud on his face. "Dr. Dunning, the instruments are waiting for you in the operating room."

"I went off duty at five and the instruments are not my responsibility," she answered. Which was true. Once off duty, in theory, she no longer had that responsibility.

He glowered at her then went away, but in a short while he was back again, demanding that she get up and take care of the instruments. Once again she answered, with a dogged stubbornness: "I am off duty and the instruments are not up to me."

This went on all evening. Walter Parsons kept hammering on her door, making his demands, and she kept refusing to budge from her position. Finally at ten o'clock she locked her door and decided that she would stand the siege behind it.

When he came again she called through the open transom over her door: "Dr. Parsons, I have told you I won't do those instruments because I am off duty. As far as I am concerned the instruments may rust at the expense of the hospital. It is bedtime and I am going to sleep. Good night!" That ended it.

The next morning she wondered at her own recklessness and she worried, too. Dr. Parsons was her superior. Would he report her for refusing to carry out his orders? And if he did that, what would happen to her?

She had a strange feeling that both questions were answered for her when, a week later, the chairman of the board of trustees of the city hospitals, Dr. John Winters Brannan, made a visit to the hospital. He had a long talk with Miss Stowers and whispers ran around the hospital. What was it all about? Why was he here?

They never knew. Nothing was ever said. But Emily was sent for and when she entered the room where Dr. Brannan and Miss Stowers were sitting, she walked with fear in her heart, sure that Dr. Parsons had made his report and that she was to be censured or dismissed. Dr. Brannan greeted her warmly, got up and offered her a chair and all he said to her was, "Is everything going all right, Dr. Dunning?"

"Yes, sir," she answered.

He glanced at Miss Stowers and back at Emily and there was a twinkle in his eye. "Hmmm. Well, that will be all, Doctor."

She wasn't fired, but she was sure about that twinkle. It gave her courage, not long afterward, to dare to do what she thought was right against all the ridicule of her four senior doctors.

Out on the ambulance she had found a man unconscious on a street corner, with the policeman bending over him. Emily could not hear any breathing but she felt for his wrist and found the pulse still fairly strong. Back to Gouverneur she raced with him and got him into a ward bed. Immediately she started artificial respiration. She and Mary Baker, the nurse, alternated since neither of them alone could keep up the manipulations, the rhythmic attempt to force the man to breathe.

There was no question about what was wrong with the man; he had opium poisoning and was in a coma. His color was blue and his pulse was getting weaker. She went in search of more help since artificial respiration was his only hope, she was sure, and that was too hard on only the two of them.

Dr. Dowling came and looked at the man. "For Heaven's sake, Doctor, don't you know when a man's cashed in? He is as good as gone, don't bother with him," he said scornfully.

"But he still has a fairly good pulse and he may respond to artificial respiration if I can keep it up," Emily answered.

The contemptuous, pitying smile she got from Dr. Dowling left no doubt in her mind as to his opinion.

She looked down at the patient. He *did* have a chance, even though he had stopped breathing and all the odds were against him. "Mary," she asked the nurse, "will you go and get help? I'm going to keep trying."

Not until later did she know that Mary Baker had gone first to the doctors' quarters for that help. She had been laughed at. "Yes, we hear Emily is trying to resurrect a dead man. Nothing doing, we are not interested."

She brought back nurses and Emily turned the artificial respiration manipulations over to them while she ransacked her brains and her memory for just what her medical books had said about opium poisoning. Emily had almost total recall. By closing her eyes, she could think first of the book, then of turning the pages, then the heading: "Opium Poisoning." Then the paragraphs and words themselves came back to her and she saw them as they appeared on the printed pages. "Get the patient breathing . . . artificial respiration . . . respira-

tory stimulation . . . flick the abdomen with wet towel . . .
warm the extremities . . . heart stimulation . . . black coffee . . .
keep patient awake and walking. . . ."

But first she had to get him breathing. Just one breath!
The nurses, taking turns, were getting very tired when suddenly a welcome group of visitors appeared. Several policemen came to get the man's story if he should recover consciousness. Without any questions, understanding what the
Lady Doctor was trying to do, they took off their coats,
rolled up their sleeves and went to work.

An hour passed and only Emily's trained eyes could see
the slightest improvement, but she knew that the blue color
was getting paler and paler, a good sign. His pulse was getting
stronger. Two hours passed. Nurses and policemen worked in
relays, never giving up. Suddenly in that quiet room came
a tiny noise that startled them all—it was a long, gasping
breath from the patient.

He was alive! Emily had no idea why flicking with a wet
towel would do any good but she grasped her towel which
had been soaked in ice water and slapped him lightly across
the abdomen. Again . . . a stinging little slap. The patient
breathed even deeper and louder, a shuddering sigh. Another
flick, another breath and another and another.

"Get him on his feet and keep him walking—" she called
out, and two husky policemen grabbed him and marched
the limp patient around the room until he began to struggle
with his feet and finally found them, even managing to
stagger with their help.

They poured him a cup of black coffee. The policemen
took him for a walk up and down the corridor and each
time they came to the door of the room, Mary Baker was
ready with another cup of coffee. To Emily's joy, the patient
began talking, wildly, about a holdup and how he had been
given "knockout drops." Someone, undoubtedly pretending
to be his friend, had given him a drink which contained

opium enough to kill him, then robbed him and left him unconscious on the street.

He would live, now. He was past danger. One of the nurses took him to a bed in a ward and Emily, Mary Baker, the other nurses and the policemen looked at one another, happy in their triumph over death. "Good work, Doc," said one of the policemen as he slipped his coat back on. "We'll be back tomorrow to get his full story."

Emily thanked them all. She couldn't begin to express her real feelings. What the nurses and the officers had done was way beyond the call of duty. They could have refused her or ignored her, especially the nurses, since the other doctors had declared the case hopeless.

In fact, she realized, she had never encountered any real hostility from the nurses. Miss Stowers hand-picked the nurses she hired and they were all exceptionally competent and intelligent; from the beginning they had been courteous to her, just as Miss Stowers had been, but at the same time watchful and wary. Now they had shown their confidence in her by wholeheartedly backing her up even when her attempt to save a life had seemed futile and ridiculous.

This was not to say that she never made mistakes. She did —and the nurses knew it. Dr. Emily Dunning was a human being, not a machine. Her training, however, had been so good; she had learned so well at Cornell and Bellevue in her earlier days; her memory was so dependable that the mistakes she did make were trivial ones and never serious enough to endanger a life.

Perhaps because one can admire a perfect machine but never love it, the nurses lost their caution and really warmed toward the Lady Doctor when she pulled a real boner and fell for an old trick.

She was on ambulance call when a policeman telephoned to say that she was urgently needed: a woman was dying on a street corner! Emily hopped on the "bus," the driver cracked his whip and away they tore, with Emily praying they would reach the street corner in time. When she arrived there, the usual crowd was gathered around the victim, with the police trying to keep back the curious and sympathetic bystanders.

"Ah, the poor thing. She's awfully sick, Doc," came the advice from the crowd as Emily pushed her way through and knelt over the writhing figure of a fairly young woman whose eyes were pleading in anguish. The pain was in her stomach and Emily probed and found what seemed to be a great tumorous mass there, a large lump that might be blocking the intestines. There was no reason to doubt either the pain, the symptoms or the lump her fingers found. She ordered the woman placed on a stretcher and put in the ambulance.

Back they raced to Gouverneur. Emily saw to it that the poor little suffering woman was placed in a bed. She then changed her ambulance suit for her white uniform, scrubbed her hands and then went to see about her new patient.

Again she probed the stomach while the woman moaned. But something seemed wrong to Emily; her sensitive fingers conveyed some kind of warning to her brain; the "tumor" was not quite what it should have been. She went on with her examination, blaming her own lack of experience. She ordered sedatives to ease the pain. The nurse on duty and Emily did their best to make the patient comfortable and then Emily sent the nurse to fetch the senior surgeon, as was customary, to look over this strange little woman with her strange tumor.

The doctor came, took one look and burst out laughing. "It's Beckie! Back with us again, Beckie? Dr. Dunning, don't you know the difference between a real tumor and a fake one? Beckie is notorious here at Gouverneur. Every time she gets a little too hungry or wants a good bed and a lot of attention, she fakes an illness or a tumor and gets brought in. And you fell for it."

Dr. Sheehan came by just then and was told the joke. He

was delighted at Emily's humiliation but suddenly surprised when she began to laugh at herself, too. Emily Dunning's laugh—so rarely heard at Gouverneur—was one of the most attractive things about her: a bubbling, rollicking laugh, so unlike the reserved, quiet and severe tone of voice she forced herself to use that the nurse glanced at her sharply, and then smiled.

After the doctors left, the nurse said, "I'm sorry, Doctor, that I didn't recognize Beckie when you brought her in. It's been some time since she was here last. You mustn't feel badly about this," she added, in the most friendly tone Emily had yet heard from any nurse, "because she fools many of the doctors. When she wants to get into a hospital and be coddled and have a lot of attention, she's an artist at faking symptoms. Why, even Dr. Erdman was taken in once; he operated on her for appendicitis when there was nothing at all wrong with her appendix."

Thus the nurses had begun to show, in whatever way they could, without openly opposing the four senior doctors, that they liked and admired Emily. The ambulance drivers were devoted to her. Another change was going on which she was somewhat slower to see: the people of the East Side, in every district, had come gradually and then, completely and passionately, to love her.

Because the small boys still ran behind the ambulance shouting, "Get a man, get a man," Emily didn't at first catch the difference in the way they called it. She didn't see the affection in the eyes of a small boy who ran after her and shouted at her, until she caught, also, those other words they chanted: "Lady Doctor! Lady Doctor!"

And then one day she saw and understood. A little boy of about five had his favorite seat on the top of a low fire hydrant where he waited to see the ambulance pass. He, too, shouted: "Lady Doctor!" But as she watched, this one day, she saw that he had trained his little pup to bow his head as she passed, and then the boy cried out, "Emilie—Emilieee!" and waved to her.

She waved back but her throat was so tight she could hardly swallow as the ambulance whisked her on out of sight. The boy loved her. She couldn't be mistaken about that.

Her eyes were opened now and she saw the smiles on the faces of the people who watched her pass. As she heard "Lady Doctor!" and "Emily" called out to her from all sides, she began to feel the warmth and pride and affection for her; no longer were her sex and her name insults to be thrown in her face.

A few days afterward she was called on an emergency to a big chocolate factory and, famished as she always was from the long hours and the hard work, she smelled the chocolate as she started to walk through the factory gates. "My, that chocolate smells good," she cried.

That night there was a box of chocolates delivered to the hospital as a gift to her, with a card that read: "For the Lady Doctor who said the chocolate smelt good."

She would walk into a poverty-stricken home and they would beg her to have a cup of tea. The politicians of the district invited her to their political clambakes. More important, the word had been passed around by the toughest of toughs in the Bowery that the Lady Doctor was to be kept safe wherever she went. So now she could walk without fear into the worst opium dens, the worst haunts of vice and depravity, step in between men who were fighting—and never be harmed.

Dr. Dowling and Dr. Parsons and Dr. Sheehan had done much to frighten her about the worst street of all—Charles Street. "The wickedest street in New York," they warned her, and waited for the day when she would be called there and be run out of it. That never happened. Emily Dunning went as freely and safely into Charles Street as she went any place else. Nevertheless, she dreaded going there, because it *was* a terrible street.

The first time she rode the "bus" there her heart was in her mouth. It was a dark place; light came to it from saloon doors that opened now and then to let out a reeling drunk. But even in their drunkenness they saw the cap she wore with Gouverneur Hospital on it and stepped aside, muttering: "Oh, the Doc, the Lady Doc," and let her pass unmolested. She had to go into one of the tenements there, dark and squalid and smelly, and she wondered what she would find at the top—a murder? a victim of dope? She was glad that the ambulance driver was coming up right behind her.

When the door opened, she had a shock; the tiny, poor little room was as clean as a pin, with almost nothing in it but the bed and the crucifix over the bed. It was stark poverty but made rich by the loving way in which a brokenhearted son was trying to help his dying mother, praying for her. There was nothing Emily could do; the mother was very old and ready to die and she needed the priest more than she needed the doctor.

With the approach of winter Emily knew that her existence and her survival at Gouverneur were more precarious than ever. In January, Walter Parsons and Jack Dowling would leave. If the new incoming interns were anything like the ones who were her juniors now, they wouldn't be interested in warfare against her. She would be an established doctor to them. So if the four were going to get rid of her they had to do it now—and Nature had put the weapon of winter into their hands.

Winter! Rains and sleet, driving winds, snowstorms and blizzards, treacherous ice; this was a New York winter. An ambulance driver for Gouverneur had to go out into it and sit unprotected and open to the weather on the back of the "bus." It was almost inhuman for a man, and certainly inconceivable that a woman could do it!

9

If the four doctors had winter on their side, Emily had allies on her side, too—the ambulance drivers, the people of the East Side, the policeman and some of the nurses. December brought wind with it and then snow, and the wind increased and sometimes the snow turned to driving particles of ice on Emily's face, but she hung onto the straps with mittened hands and bent her face deep into the collar of her mackintosh. When the cold became almost too much for her, Dick Bateman always took the route past Still's Oyster House. He'd run in and bring out two piping-hot roast beef sandwiches. He would take one, she the other and they would eat them, all the while stamping their feet to keep warmth in them. The hot food always revived her.

Herman, the orderly in charge of the kitchen at Gouverneur, broke the rules to slip her hot coffee and hot buttered toast when she came late at night, frozen and stiff.

Actually, by this time she had accumulated enough seniority so that she shouldn't have been on "first call" for the ambulance; at least, not constantly. It was deliberate injustice and the whole hospital knew it, yet the house physician had the authority to make out the schedules and there it was, night after night: Dr. Dunning—First Call, Ambulance.

In every little way possible the nurses and the ambulance drivers and the orderlies tried to look after her and protect her when they could. Emily was strong and healthy but the cold rides on the ambulance and the constant fatigue from never getting enough sleep were eating away at her strength.

She worried mostly that she might become so numb and dazed that her mind would play tricks on her and she would make a wrong diagnosis of a patient, prescribe the wrong treatment, or that her skillful hands would shake when she was doing an emergency surgery. The fear stalked her when she was awake and haunted the brief hours she had for sleep.

"I can't stand it another day; I will report them," she cried to her mother. Mrs. Dunning knew her own daughter too well not to know this was a momentary weakness and that Emily would despise herself if she ran to the Medical Board with complaints. So she soothed her and strengthened her: "Control yourself, Emily, you can stand it."

"Yes," Emily answered wearily. "I can stand it. I can hold on until January. Walter Parsons and Jack Dowling will be leaving then and I will move up to the senior position. Jerry Sheehan and Dick Speed will be house physician and house surgeon but they won't dare keep me on first call then."

They did dare! Parsons and Dowling left but the other two broke all precedent and rules. Dr. Dunning might be a senior surgeon but they kept the schedule unchanged: First Call, Dr. Dunning.

Throughout January the weather worsened. There were storms and blizzards and Emily rode the bus with the full weight of them slashing her face and body. Nor was there any peace for her at mealtimes. To instruct and entertain the new subjunior doctors, Dr. Dosh and Dr. Henderson, her persecutors told them long, detailed accounts of gruesome hospital cases and—with one eye on Emily—told these stories of rape, of burned bodies, of horrifying wounds, in the coarsest of language.

One evening Emily reached the end of her strength. She had been on ambulance call all Friday night. Saturday morning, as she was thinking longingly of her bed, she was told she must stay on first call—all that day and that evening, too. The most she could get were a few quick cat naps in between. The hours became an endless blur, of rushing out into the bitter cold, forcing herself to be wide awake and alert when she examined the patient, drowsing on the open back seat of the ambulance returning to the hospital, waking with a start to realize that if she did fall asleep she could be killed rolling off the ambulance.

Then she would come back into the warmth of the hospital, which numbed her as much as the cold had.

By Sunday morning she was dead on her feet but she had to keep going all day. Those were her orders. Even in her sleepy state of mind she sensed an unusual solicitude for her: Herman brought her more and stronger cups of coffee, the ambulance drivers tucked the blanket carefully around her legs and asked at every stop, "You all right, Doc?"

I'm all right, she thought. *I can make it through this day and then I can sleep*. Sleep was almost an agonizing thing to think about; she wanted it so much.

When she was finally off duty that Sunday evening, when she arrived on her last trip and walked into Gouverneur so cold she could hardly stand, she was given curt orders that there was an "emergency case. Report at once to operating room to give an anesthetic."

Emily Dunning had been on call now for sixty hours straight. She had a strange feeling as if she were floating, not walking, into the operating room. She scrubbed her hands, took the anesthesia and the cone, put the cone over the patient's face and began letting the anesthesia drip through it.

The room was quiet and peaceful and warm. The surgeon had not yet come in. Emily stood over the patient and the heat of the room penetrated into her fatigued body and, insensibly, she relaxed. Still standing over the patient, her head over the anesthesia cone, she felt herself drifting away, farther and farther. She was glad she was going . . . glad because it meant she could sleep and sleep forever.

Someone grabbed her arm. Startled, she came to and saw that Mary Baker, the nurse, was shaking her and pulling her arm away. And then Emily knew what was happening . . . she was chloroforming herself by inhaling the fumes! A second later—and she would have been unconscious on the floor; the visiting surgeon would have found her like that and she would have been in disgrace, if not much worse.

Mary Baker's face was tender and sweet with anxiety in her desire to help Emily. She took her into the sterilizing room and forced coffee into her until Emily had pulled herself completely together and was able to go out, briskly, to meet the surgeon and see to her patient.

That night Emily *knew* that she would make it. With such loving protection and help as she was getting, she would pull through and nothing whatever was going to stop her. She could stand up to it all because she was not alone; she was surrounded by her allies.

Both Dr. Sheehan and Dr. Speed must have sensed something different in her from then on, or perhaps they, too, were growing tired of the warfare. Perhaps they knew that they had already gone down to defeat. They let up the pressure on her just a little, and the next evening at the dinner table, when the talk turned to a particularly distasteful case, Dr. Sheehan stopped it, saying that was not something to be discussed while they were eating.

The weeks and the months flew by. An emergency hospital is always a strenuous place for a doctor to work in, and Emily was kept busy . . . but not beyond the power of her endurance.

Then it was the last of June and the last day at Gouverneur for both Dr. Sheehan and Dr. Speed. Emily contributed to the present which was always given to departing doctors and she was courteous and polite all during their farewell dinner. If she was gay that night, it wasn't just because it was a social occasion for her—it was deliverance!

And the next day Dr. Emily Dunning was officially house surgeon.

The newspapers, as usual, made much of this. For the first time a woman had been appointed house surgeon in a city hospital. They made much of the fact that she, as a woman, would be ordering about and directing the work of the men doctors under her.

This was unimportant to Emily. What was important was that she had reached the goal she had set for herself; she had demonstrated that a woman was as good a doctor for a general hospital as a man; *and she had not broken her vow and complained, not once!*

The whole of the East Side sent in its congratulations by jubilant messages which reached her through the ambulance drivers, the doctors and the patients. The nurses showed their complete willingness to work under her and some were even overjoyed. The other doctors on the staff accepted her nonchalantly, which was the best way of all, because it was as if they were saying: What's all the fuss about? Dr. Dunning is a fine surgeon. Why shouldn't she have the promotion? They would never know that Emily had been afraid, until that last day of June, that the Medical Board would be wary about giving her the position.

Telephone calls and notes came from Dr. Jacobi and from Miss Anna Brackett, her first schoolteacher; from Uncle Henry at Cornell, and from all the people who had helped her or wished her well or had been pulling for her. Major Zalinski took the keenest personal pride in Dr. Emily Dunning, house surgeon, and her family and Ben waited impatiently for her day off so they could celebrate.

The responsibility she faced was enormous but she felt so happy and so free that she would have welcomed even more. Yet it was a big boost to her morale when the eminent Dr. John G. Kelly, who would be visiting surgeon for the month of July, welcomed her into the operating room that first day with a twinkle in his eye and the words:

"And I understand, Dr. Dunnin', that today you will be becomin' house surgeon; well, there is one thing I want yer to understand—no matter whether yer kill a man or not, I shall stand back of yer." And he offered a hand for a hearty shake.

His Irish brogue and his teasing words bridged the gap between his experienced authority and her brand-new and trembling assumption of authority. Each of the three months in which she would be house surgeon there would be a new visiting surgeon whom she would assist. She was in complete charge of all minor surgical cases and would perform these herself.

The first week proved her fitness, and Dr. Kelly was more than satisfied as they worked together on a variety of operations. When her day off came and she could go home for the family celebration, she was in a jubilant mood.

The Dunning family had plenty to celebrate that day. Will was to marry Ruth Morse very shortly; he was already in practice as a dentist and proving himself to be an exceptionally good one. Margaret, president of her class at Vassar, was engaged to Charles Day, a young engineer from Philadelphia. Amy kept an eye on them all—how many times, in the darkest of Emily's struggles, had she been heartened by the arrival at Gouverneur of a package of cookies and fruit and other delicacies from Amy! Ned was in school and Harry was making a brilliant record at Cornell and would get his degree that year, 1904, from the New York College of Dentistry.

Emily and Ben formally announced their engagement that day.

Of course the family had known it for these past years but now they could all definitely talk of plans for the wedding.

Ben would finish his internship in a month; he would then go to Vienna, Austria, to finish up his studies, and when he returned the wedding would take place.

If there was a flaw in Emily's happiness it was this. She and Ben both hated the idea of the separation while he was abroad, and ever since she had known he was going she had wanted to go, too. American colleges and hospitals still lagged a bit behind the big European medical centers in the most advanced knowledge and techniques; it was the dream of all devoted American physicians or surgeons to polish off their education with studies in Europe.

Just the same, she was determined not to let this one regret spoil her perfect day. With Ben and the entire Dunning family gathered together, the house rang with laughter and jokes, buzzed with talk. Then they all fell silent because Mrs. Dunning had something to say to them. They were outside, drinking lemonade under the pear tree, and they gathered in a circle around Mama's chair.

"Wedding presents," she said in her gentle voice, "should not be given until just before the wedding day, but we are going to make an exception in the case of Emily and Ben. We are going to give them their present now—" and she handed Emily a slip of paper.

It was a check and attached to it was a note: For your trip to Vienna with Ben.

Emily looked, unbelieving, at all the faces around her and she knew that the whole family had been in on the secret. As a matter of fact, not only family but close friends had insisted on contributing to the wedding trip present.

This was all she needed to make her happiness complete. Her cup was running over. Now she would not have to wait for their marriage until Ben returned. Ben would go to Vienna now. When her term at Gouverneur was finished in January, she would join him and they would be married there. They would have this glorious honeymoon and, in addition, they would both study under the finest of teachers.

Her three months' tenure as house surgeon flew. She had the privilege of serving, alternately, with Dr. Kelly, Dr. John F. Erdman and Dr. Louis J. Ladin—three of the best surgeons in New York City and she acquitted herself well in their eyes. Especially was she grateful for the chance to work with Erdman, who was a master of the most difficult and delicate of operations.

When September came and Dr. Louis J. Ladin took over the role of visiting surgeon, it was natural that they would have more cases of a gynecological nature—difficult childbirths, Cesareans, etc.—than other type of cases because Dr. Ladin was famous for his skill in these. When private doctors on the East Side knew he was operating at Gouverneur, they sent all their problem cases to him.

It was during this month that Emily decided on her future practice. She would specialize in gynecological surgery. It was the work that most interested her.

In October the final change was made and she and Dr. Batchelder switched positions and she became *chief of staff* at Gouverneur. Except for the authority of the visiting physicians, she ruled supreme. She made out the schedules for all the other doctors; she presided at the head of the table during mealtimes.

With the position also went full responsibility for every department, every activity at Gouverneur, and she was then only twenty-eight years old!

There was no danger of her getting puffed up with her own importance. Only on the rarest of occasions did she ride the ambulance, but every once in a while she slipped across the street to the stable, irresistibly drawn back. She and the drivers talked while she patted the sleek noses of Jim or Stockings or good-natured Babe who nibbled affectionately at her sleeve. Dick Bateman would say: "Remember, Doc, that night we went to Charles Street?" and Murray would interrupt: "Remember Beckie and how she fooled us?" or Tom White would chuckle: "Everywhere I go they still want to know how the Lady Doctor is getting along."

It was good to come here and remember these things and remind herself that the ambulance was the life line to Gouverneur, and that her juniors were going through hardships and the kind of experiences that were terrifying, agonizing and exhausting. She would do what she could to encourage them, not break their spirit as others had tried to do to her.

In the medical wards, the great terrors of that day and age were the contagious diseases. Medical science had not yet developed the serums and antitoxins and the injections which could immunize an entire population against diphtheria, typhoid and those other killers. It was the age of a medical world beginning to open up to discoveries, but it was only the beginning.

An epidemic of cerebrospinal meningitis hit the East Side and the ambulances began bringing in stricken patients day after day, hour after hour. Emily and her staff were working around the clock in the wards and, to add to their worries, there was then no known protection for themselves. They lived in the heart of the danger, agonizing over their poor, suffering patients, constantly exposed so that at any minute one of them might come down with the illness.

Every morning at breakfast, it became a habit with them to test their own necks. Was there any stiffness? This was the symptom they dreaded in the onslaught of the meningitis. It was a weird picture: seven young men and one young woman gingerly feeling their necks and turning and rotating them, but it was not funny.

She longed for Ben. He was in Vienna, accompanied by his mother, who had made a quick trip over and would be coming back in a few days. Emily had not fully realized to what extent Ben had strengthened her by that one day a week they could spend together. How he could comfort, advise, help, and with his many interests, pull her out of too great an absorption in what was happening at Gouverneur. But Ben was in Vienna.

The epidemic was still raging and the wards were full when Mrs. Barringer returned to New York. She was struck the very next day with a heart attack and died that night. It was so sudden and so unexpected, and Emily was so fond of her that the shock of it was stunning.

Ben cabled he would return immediately. Emily had to go on with the responsibilities at Gouverneur and those responsibilities had to take precedence over her own personal sorrow. She could not put Mrs. Barringer's death out of her mind, or the grief that Ben must be feeling, but there were all the patients at Gouverneur who needed her, and every single minute there were decisions that only she could make.

The load of suffering and death weighed down every day. Then, gradually, the epidemic was checked and the load lightened; the hospital returned to normal—and Ben arrived home.

It was a sad homecoming for him and Emily wondered if their plans for going to Vienna had changed.

Indeed, they hadn't. Ben was more determined than ever and Mrs. Dunning and Mr. Barringer backed him up; there was no need to wait until January of 1905. They could go now, be married here in New York and take ship immediately afterward for Europe.

"You've accumulated time off because you took no vacation these past summers," he told Emily. "That means you have the right to be graduated from Gouverneur in the middle of December, and I'm asking you to say yes and marry me—and we'll sail Christmas Day. For once, our own personal plans come first."

Gladly and with a clear conscience, she did as he asked; applied for the time off and it was readily granted. She would receive her diploma the week before Christmas. When the announcement was made at the hospital she became aware of an immediate and unusual stir of activity: the comings and goings of politicians from the East Side, whisperings that broke off when she appeared.

The night before she left, she was given a grand farewell dinner and a gift of surgical instruments by her staff of doctors. It was a fine evening and afterward she went through the hospital saying good-by to everyone, and especially to her favorites: Mary Baker and Herman, the kitchen orderly, and Martin and the rest. She heard nice things said about her and knew they were sincere.

When she said good-by to Miss Stowers, for just a second the cool, disciplined mask that wonderful woman always wore slipped a bit. Emily thought she saw behind it a genuine affection for her—which she certainly felt for Miss Stowers.

The next day she awoke in her own bedroom at home, feeling it was all unreal. Gouverneur had been her life for so long. She and her mother plunged immediately into sorting and planning her clothes for the trip, but Emily had a feeling of waiting and suspense, a premonition that it was not yet all over. Something more was going to happen that evening. The ambulance drivers had said they were going to "drop over" to her house.

When the doorbell rang Mrs. Dunning ordered Emily to wait for her guests in the still-elegant gray velvet parlor. She was standing there, expecting a nice little evening with her friends, the drivers, when it seemed to her as if the whole of the East Side came crowding into the room.

Not all the people from that vast area of the East Side could come, of course, but they had sent their delegation to represent them. The ambulance drivers came first, then policemen, politicians, settlement workers and a sprinkling of ordinary citizens, they filled the parlor to overflowing.

Emily would have welcomed them and circulated around the room to talk to each one of them, but they would not have it. This was a solemn occasion. Their spokesman had a speech to make:

"Dr. Dunning: We take great pleasure in stating that we are a committee selected by a large number of citizens and policemen of New York City to tender you this set of resolutions as a token of the high esteem in which we hold you as a friend."

Lady Doctor! Lady Doctor!—behind the solemn words of the speech Emily heard in her own mind the chant of all those boys calling after her and the friendly yells from the people on the street: *Lady Doctor!*

The spokesman was going on: ". . . you, by courage, hard work and independence have broken down a prejudice . . . and have attained a place in the front rank of . . . prominent physicians of this country. The idea of this presentation arose with the Ambulance Drivers of Gouverneur Hospital. . . ."

Emily missed the next words as she looked at her best friends. Tears brimmed so that she could hardly see Dick Bateman's happy face or Tom White's or Murray's.

". . . in conclusion," the spokesman was saying, "on behalf of all concerned in this presentation, from the professional man to the laborer, from the housewife to the professional woman, let me say God speed you in your chosen career, and God bless you!"

Then the great moment had arrived and he took a step forward and handed Emily the large, inscribed paper, mounted under a frame of glass. She bent her head and read:

TESTIMONIAL

from the

Citizens of New York

the Police of the 7th, 12th, and 13th precincts,

and the Ambulance Drivers of Gouverneur Hospital

to

DR. EMILY DUNNING

upon her retirement, January 1, 1905 as

Chief of Staff of Gouverneur Hospital, New York

Dr. Dunning

for two years has served the hospital and the people of New York in a manner that has won the admiration and esteem of her fellow-workers and of all those with whom she has been brought in contact. Her wonderful skill, conscientious and untiring efforts, charm of manner, devotion to her patients, extreme kindness and consideration for all who labored with her, have endeared her to all.

As the only woman ambulance surgeon in the world she has won distinction that is world-wide and has brought honor, not only upon herself, but upon her sex, her profession, Gouverneur Hospital and the City of New York.

We hope and pray that the future may hold happiness and additional honors in store for her, and our best wishes follow her in her new labors.

By now Emily Dunning was frankly crying with joy and gratitude and the moment threatened to break her down completely. Amy and Mrs. Dunning saved the day by bringing in refreshments. The large crowd took sandwiches and coffee and broke up into little groups, making it easier for Emily to come to each one of them and thank them, and also sparing her from having to make a speech in answer. If she had tried to do that, she wouldn't have been able to say a word, she was so emotionally wrought up.

When she came to the drivers she wanted to embrace them, but she preserved their dignity by just shaking hands.

"You've no idea, Doc," said Dick Bateman, "the uproar all this caused in the East Side. Everyone had to have his say; some wanted to give you a watch, instead, and some wanted some other thing. But we finally decided on the resolution." He took a swallow of coffee. "And when it came to letting people contribute! Everyone wanted to give his penny or two but we drew the line. It was no use them crooks and drunken bums or anyone who owned a saloon saying to us: 'The Lady Doc's our friend, too.' No sir, we wouldn't take their money. They were threatening to beat us up but we weren't going to have their dirty money paying for your resolution."

As she happily circled the room and said "good-by" and "thank you" to all these people she had worked with, Emily missed one little, tiny figure. But he was there just the same in her memory: the little boy who sat on the fire hydrant and taught his pup to bow his head when she passed and who waved to her and called out: "Emilie—Emilieeee!" and had given her heart a lift when she had most needed it.

She and Ben were quietly married by the Reverend Percy Grant at the Church of the Ascension on December 24th and they sailed on Christmas Day, on the *Kroonland* for Europe.

To some people, it might have seemed a strange honeymoon for these two highly trained doctors to plunge back into their student days and to fill these first months of their married life with medical talk and scribblings in notebooks and attending lectures, but to Dr. Benjamin Barringer and Dr. Emily Dunning Barringer it was the happiest and most natural thing in the world.

Both now knew what their direction in medical work was taking: Ben into urology and Emily into gynecology. Some of the lectures they attended were the same, and for the others they went their own way during the day and met in the evening to compare notes.

It wasn't all work, of course. There was the whole beautiful city of Vienna to explore. They would walk and sight-see, then they would stop and rest while Ben captured the beauty of a magnificent arched stone doorway in paints and oils on his canvas while Emily sat quietly and at peace by his side. Afterward they would stroll back to their lodginghouse and perhaps stop in at some café where they could hear laughter and violins playing.

They thought they knew each other so well after all these years, but to their delight they noticed new things. Ben was surprised at Emily's love for words; the way she would search in her vivid imagination for just the right word to use, as if she loved its very sound. An object was "pristine" to her or it was "ignominious"—never just plain "clear" or "mean."

And she had never fully realized how marvelously he could switch off his intense, scientific mind and open it again to the beauty of a wall or a doorway or the color of a tree or a cloud. A brilliant, searching mind, the soul of an artist and the body of a fine athlete—that was her husband.

When they returned to New York, positions were waiting for them. While she was still at Gouverneur, she had been offered a position on Dr. Ladin's gynecological staff at New York Polyclinic Hospital and she had accepted. In this, she would be an attending surgeon, just as Ben was an attending surgeon at St. Vincent's Hospital, and he would, later on, be assistant attending surgeon at Bellevue, attending urologist at the New York Infirmary for Women and Children, and the Nassau and Nyack and the Mary McClellan hospitals and —finally, in 1920—the attending urologist at Memorial Hospital.

But that was in the future. This was 1905. They rented a house at 118 East Eighteenth Street in which they lived upstairs and opened their offices downstairs for their private practice. It turned out to be a good division: she had morning work at her hospital, and used the offices in the afternoon; he did just the opposite.

And there they settled down to what they hoped would be long and peaceful and happy lives.

10

Their lives were happy and richly satisfying and never placid or dull. They were both too energetic and too adventurous ever to be dull.

During the years between 1905 and 1914, Ben laid the groundwork for his later reputation as one of the leading urologists in the country. In addition, he managed to keep up his interests in sports and in the arts.

As for Emily, it was typical of her that she should become interested in the one subject which was practically forbidden.

This was the age of the horse and carriage, although more and more of those "horseless carriages" were coming in and people were actually driving forty miles an hour when they speeded! Men wore bowler hats or hard hats and women's clothes trailed to the ground. Silk stockings had come into fashion, but a proper lady never showed her ankles; in fact, she blushed when someone referred to a leg because she didn't have them; she had limbs. Ladies were sheltered. There were so many things one didn't speak about, not even in a whisper.

It was in this kind of atmosphere that Dr. Emily Dunning Barringer bluntly said that venereal disease was something to be talked about. It had to be talked about, she claimed, so that the general public appreciated its dangers and those who were afflicted with it could conquer their shame and come to hospitals for treatment.

Silence on this subject was a crime, she declared. Ignorance was worse. As a gynecologist she saw women who had inno-cently and unknowingly contracted the disease and were too ignorant or too embarrassed to come to a hospital until it was too late. Some venereal diseases were congenital and she saw young children doomed from their birth to a life of misery.

She was at least thirty years ahead of her time. The day *would* come when newspapers and magazines spoke freely on venereal diseases and encouraged education on the subject. When that did happen it was because of the work of such people as Emily and other courageous people.

No newspaper would touch such a subject in her pioneer days. So she made laboratory studies and published papers in medical journals, and she kept after the city's Department of Health. Here there were several doctors who were even ahead of her in their desire to enlighten the public, but there were some who raised their hands in horror.

Emily didn't care. She went right on working. Time would prove her to be right.

In addition to their hospital work, their independent re-searches, both she and Ben began slowly to accumulate a good private practice, and by the time their son Benjamin Lang Barringer was born—and later, their daughter Emily Verona, called Velona—they were able to move to a lovely home on West End Avenue.

They were good parents. Loving, thoughtful, kind, with a sense of humor to spice their sense of responsibility; they were the kind of parents children needed. A housekeeper was hired so that meals would be prompt and good, teeth would be brushed, the children would never be left alone and unat-tended—but it was in the evening that Ben and Emily could make of themselves a real family of four.

Then they could listen with full attention to a school problem or a squabble that had to be settled or whether a new dress was really needed, and then they would take the time and trouble to lead the young minds of their children into whatever channels interested them, encouraging every bit of talent or inclination.

They were wise in not trying to force either of their children to become doctors. Ben was happy as a doctor but he never forgot the pangs it had cost him to give up his dreams of a career as an artist. If the children wanted to be artists or lawyers or bricklayers, then by all means they should be— but they should be good ones.

The year 1914 ushered in the holocaust of World War I. During the time of the war their focus was entirely changed and their thoughts were of those thousands wounded, ill and dying on the battlefields. Emily had joined the American Medical Women's Association and now they formed a committee, under the name of the American Women's Hospitals, to raise money for the purchase of ambulances to send aboard.

Who better than Dr. Emily Dunning Barringer, the first woman doctor in New York to ride an ambulance, could spearhead such a campaign so close to her heart? An ambulance was borrowed and she rode up and down Wall Street— there was more money there than on Charles Street in the East Side!—calling out, making speeches, begging for the money. It came in; the ambulances were purchased and sent to battlefields where they were most needed.

After the war the King of Serbia sent Emily a decoration for her part in this undertaking.

Overshadowing everything, however, was Harry's—Dr. Harry Dunning, now—departure for the war as a surgical dentist.

Harry had just married. He had a fine position with the Presbyterian Hospital. Some of his fellow doctors thought he was stupid and crazy to throw away his opportunities there, to go and help the war wounded, especially since the United States was not yet in the war.

But Eleine Chatillon, his exquisitely beautiful young bride, was proud of him and so were all of the Dunnings. They thought it was typical of the warmhearted and gallant Harry that he should volunteer to go, even though he would be far behind in promotion and in his career when he returned. Those who stayed home in their jobs had the best chance.

Ben couldn't go. He was thirty-nine in 1914. Emily was thirty-eight. Ben had two children and heavy responsibility in his hospital work.

They saw Harry off, in his new medical uniform, on a somber, dark night and watched him and the rest of the Presbyterian Hospital Unit, all volunteers, march in most unmilitary fashion aboard the ship that would take them to England. There was nothing to do then but wait for his letters. His unit was first attached to the British Army and then later, when America entered the war, to the American Expeditionary Force. His letters home were full of his own cheerful good humor, when he spoke of himself, but they were also full of serious medical talk. Pulling teeth and filling teeth were routine; what engaged his whole interest was the possibility of repairing smashed jaws and faces which bullets had ripped to pieces.

Emily and Ben read the letters and they could see between the lines that Harry was doing a pioneer work and study. He visited maxillary surgery centers in France and in England, studied what they were doing for the repair of faces and jaws, and worked out his own technique, improving on what he had seen, and was finally placed in charge of this highly important maxillary facial service at the base hospital in Vichy, France.

When the war was over and Captain Harry Dunning came home, the Dunnings and Ben and Emily wisely allowed him to have his first meeting alone with Eleine. On the second night they all gathered at the Barringers and waited.

From the windows they could see a very trim, very military figure striding up the street with his lovely wife clinging to his arm. A moment later he was engulfed by them all and it was at least ten minutes later that all the doctors at this family gathering had forgotten separation and homecoming and were plunged into medical talk.

They wanted so much to know about this new technique of Harry's.

"It was not only the physical suffering that appalled me and made me determine never to be satisfied with a mere repair job," he told them. "I could have patched them up somehow. But I could never forget that these men would not always be soldiers. The world would not always think of them as heroes. The day would come when people would look at them and shudder and turn away."

He was so modest under his self-confidence that he could talk about his work without self-consciousness. He was never aware that he had done anything special.

"Who would look at them? Who would marry them? Give them jobs? They couldn't just be patched up any old way; they had to be given good, pleasant—even handsome—faces. If possible, the rehabilitation of those smashed faces had to be as nearly like their old ones as possible."

It was a relatively new science, plastic surgery, and Harry Dunning was one of the first to use modern methods and develop new techniques.

His mother warned him that night: "You will have every rich, vain old woman running to you to have you change her face so she will look youthful again."

He laughed. "I'll tell them: why don't you grow old grace-fully? Perhaps I could change their faces but I can't do any-thing about their paunchy stomachs or their wrinkled hands. No, plastic surgery will be as important in peacetime as it was in the war, but I'll save my efforts for those poor un-fortunate people whose scars are twisting and deforming their whole lives."

Emily thought that night that it was not really surprising that Harry had proved all of them wrong who said his going to war would harm his career. With his stick-to-itive quality and his feeling for humanity, it was not surprising that he had found an extraordinary work, a new career in an extraordinary field.

The years between World War I and World War II were uneventful except for the steady rise in all of their careers.

Dr. Benjamin Barringer was appointed attending urologist at Memorial Hospital in 1920. He was recognized as one of the pioneer urologists in America in cystoscopy and in the implantation of radium in cancer of the bladder. He became a Fellow of the American Medical Association and of the American College of Surgeons; a member of the New York Academy of Medicine, associated with the American Genitourinary Surgeons' group and, many years later, in 1943 he was made president of their society.

In the midst of this busy life he found time to institute the New York Physician's Art Club. There were many doctors like himself, amateur painters, and it meant a great deal to all of them to get together and encourage each other in this form of creative expression.

Dr. Henry (Harry) Dunning became attending oral surgeon at the Manhattan Eye, Ear and Throat Hospital; consulting oral surgeon at Kingsbridge Veteran and at Nassau in Long Island, at Roosevelt Hospital, at the Ruptured and Crippled Children's Hospital, and others. His work in plastic surgery brought him fame and, as had been predicted, it also brought him the vain and conceited and foolish but he would have none of them.

Will Dunning, too, was achieving prominence as an oral surgeon. He and his brother Henry helped found the brand-new School of Dental and Oral Surgery at Columbia University.

At the same time that she was assistant attending gynecologist at the New York Polyclinic Hospital, Emily had been associated with the New York Infirmary for Women and

Children, as attending surgeon. After World War I she became an attending surgeon at Kingston Avenue Hospital and then its director of gynecology. She was a member of the American Medical Women's Association and also of the American Medical Association, which included both men and women. She was a Fellow of the American College of Surgeons and of the New York Academy of Medicine.

When they all gathered either at the Barringers or the Dunnings for an evening, there were not only four doctors but five, because Ted Barringer, Ben's older brother, was also a doctor. Naturally the talk was full of the excitement of their medical lives.

"I had an operation two weeks ago," Harry would say, "that really had me scared—scared of failing a ten-year-old boy whose whole fate rested on that operation. That poor child was one of Nature's worst tricks; he had a cleft palate, a harelip and a tooth that stuck out straight like the horn of a rhinoceros. With that face he was doomed to tragedy. He was being treated like an idiot. His father thought he was cursed and wouldn't even allow him to sit with the family for his meals. I promised that boy that if he trusted in me and let me operate, he'd be the best-looking kid in his school. No question about it, I was scared—of letting him down."

"And what happened?" asked Ben.

There was a modest twinkle in Harry's eyes. "He's the best-looking kid in his school—today."

The talk turned to those moments of terror and fright that every doctor faces. Someone asked Emily which was her worst scare. She had to think a while. There had been so many at Gouverneur. Then she laughed.

"I think the worst of all was the time I was riding the ambulance and we found a man, with two policemen standing over him. The man was so drunk that he was having delirium tremens and the police were just barely able to hold him down. For a moment I didn't know what to do. I had to take him in the ambulance to the hospital. For once I didn't try to play a lone hand; I told the policemen they had to go with me and they called in two more. Even so, it took the four of them and me to hold that man down in the ambulance, and several times I thought he had wriggled through our hands and would jump out of the "bus." He was seeing snakes and other crawling things all over the floor and the blankets and all over him."

She sighed and went on. "There were cases a lot worse that I had to handle later on, but I was new on the ambulance then and all I could think of was: If it takes five of us, what is going to happen when someday I'll have to control a delirium tremens patient all by myself? Luckily, I never had to find out."

These were indeed happy and fruitful years for all of them. The only grief that came was when Mrs. Dunning died in 1922. Even though she grieved, Emily Dunning Barringer had seen so much death that it was not shocking to her any more. She had seen so many people die in bitterness, or after futile and ill-spent, frivolous or criminal lives, that she accepted Mama's death as the natural end to a rich and useful life, and was glad Mama had lived to see her children successful.

The years sped by; Ben and Emily were more and more involved in their careers; the children were growing up; life was good.

Then came 1932, marking a happy change in their way of life. Now that their son Benjamin was finishing his studies at Cornell and would soon be a practicing lawyer, with his own life to lead, and their daughter Velona was attending the Yale Art School, Dr. Emily and Dr. Benjamin Barringer found themselves longing more and more for a retreat for themselves. New York had changed. It was all bustle and vastness, noise and confusion.

They were in their fifties. Their medical practices were as flourishing as ever. Both were still rising in eminence and commanding splendid positions in the hospitals. But for their private lives they wanted peace.

They found it in a beautiful old home and grounds in New Canaan, Connecticut, and they spent long and pleasant hours remodeling it to suit themselves. From it they commuted to New York every day.

In the evenings they had the quiet of the countryside and on week ends Dr. Benjamin could paint to his heart's content and Dr. Emily could enjoy herself making plans to change this room or that one. It was a perfect life—especially when Dr. Henry Dunning and his wife and children also moved nearby in New Canaan.

The years went by. Though there was to be no flagging of her fierce energy and she became famous for her fighting spirit at the bedside of patients, willing them to live, defying death every step of the way, Dr. Emily was convinced that life was asking all it could of her and never again would it demand or force her into the limelight of public attention.

Her son married and became a successful lawyer. Velona was now Mrs. Egar Zell Steever; her husband was an artist. They had bought and now lived in the house next door to Dr. Emily and Dr. Ben. Grandchildren were born.

In 1941 Emily was elected to a term as president of the American Medical Women's Association. She was sixty-five years old. She had risen to the highest office other women doctors could give her.

But fate was not ready to let Dr. Emily rest on her laurels or in quiet work. She was once more to be thrust into the hurly-burly of public storm and strife. World War II came and America knew it must arm against the possibility of being drawn into it.

As soon as America began preparing for the threat of war men doctors were gladly received into the Army Medical

Corps and gladly given officer's rank. They were lieutenants and captains and majors right from the beginning. There was a sound reason for this. They had to be in a position where the orders they gave were obeyed; sometimes a man's life depended on that order.

For the first time in history there were women troops serving in both the Navy and the Army. And women doctors were invited, not as officers, or even into the service itself. They would be "contract" doctors, hired as civilians, with no rank, no authority, no rights. They would be in the strange position of instructing an Army nurse who might be a captain and yet the woman doctor was a person with no rank.

Dr. Emily saw the enemy—prejudice—once more and once more sailed into battle. This was as bad as her early days of struggle to get into Gouverneur Hospital. In a way it was worse, because this was 1942 and the old, bad days of treating women doctors as outsiders, as inferiors, was supposed to have been changed.

She was former president of the American Medical Women's Association so it was natural for her to turn to this powerful group. The association formed a special committee of which she was chairman, and the purpose was to secure officers' commissions in the Army and Navy for women doctors.

The opening moves of the committee met with an obstinate and firm "NO." The appeal was made to both Secretary of the Army Stimson and Secretary of the Navy Knox, and the answer was still no.

The attitude of Secretary of War Stimson really provoked Dr. Emily. She had expected sympathetic understanding from him; she felt close to him because one of her most admired teachers of surgery at Cornell University Medical College had been his father, Dr. Lewis A. Stimson. And the War Secretary's own niece, Dr. Barbara Stimson, was now a major in the Royal Army Medical Corps of England where she had gone just because she could not get the same justice from the American Army!

Actually, both the Army and Navy secretaries were help-less to do anything. This they explained to Dr. Emily's com-mittee. They had asked for a ruling of the law and the Attor-ney-General of the United States had given the law a careful reading and handed down his interpretation: The law said women doctors could not hold officers' ranks.

Well, then, the law itself would have to be changed! The committee changed the focal point of their attack onto the Senate and House of Representatives, who made the nation's laws and who could change them. The committee secured the help and services of the very distinguished woman lawyer, and former Justice, Dorothy Kenyon of New York City.

For months and months the campaign was kept up and the pressures increased, by petitions, by statements to the news-papers, by appeals, by wires and letters and telephone calls to prominent people. Miss Kenyon's legal mind showed how the law could be changed and this information was particu-larly given to those senators and representatives who were sympathetic.

Though prohibited from their rightful ranks, women doc-tors did not boycott the service. They joined as "civilian contract" doctors and were advised to do so by the special committee.

"I feel strongly," Dr. Emily Barringer said in a newspaper interview, "that women physicians must accept any position offered them by the War Department. Then, at some later date, we can help them obtain their well-deserved rank in the Medical Reserve Corps."

But there was no question as to how they felt about such "contract" positions for women surgeons and physicians. Dorothy Kenyon put it strongly, calling it "an insult to pro-fessional people to accept . . . positions as 'contract' surgeons. There should be no differentiation between the sexes."

Their campaign went on all through the year 1942. In December of that year The New York *Times*, of December 10, 1942, headlined a story which showed that the committee, of which Dr. Barringer was chairman, was appealing to the highest authority in the land:

WOMEN DOCTORS
FIGHT SERVICE BAR

Plead directly to President
to remove barrier placed
by Army and Navy

But it wasn't until April of 1943 that the first signs of success began to show. On April 13th the *Times* reprinted:

SENATE VOTES RANK
TO WOMEN DOCTORS

The Sparkman bill to commission women physicians and surgeons in the Medical Corps of the Army and Navy, which was passed by unanimous consent vote in the House last week, was passed today by voice vote in the Senate and sent to the White House. . . .

The women were jubilant. There was no doubt but that the President would sign the bill. Already the Navy had been quietly circulating questionnaires through the mail to many women surgeons, hoping to jump the gun on the Army and get the cream of the crop of these doctors for the Navy.

There was an immense amount of paper work for Dr. Emily to do in winding up the committee's work. Now the Committee had disbanded, and she was thinking with pleasure of the days of relaxation ahead with no more committee meetings, no more frantic messages back and forth between Washington, D.C., and her home in New Canaan when she received a message which astounded her.

She was invited to be present, in the White House, when President Roosevelt signed the Sparkman bill.

For such a historic moment she would gladly go once more, as she had so often trudged, wearily, defeatedly, to Washington. She and several other members of the committee were ushered into the White House study; they were met with cordial friendliness by a President terribly burdened and care-worn but as jubilant as they. Precious and much-needed, highly skilled and intelligent forces—the women doctors—were now to be added to the war effort which meant so much to President Franklin Delano Roosevelt.

He thanked Dr. Emily and the others for bringing this happy event about. Then they watched as the bill was put before him on his desk, as he reached for a pen and wrote his famous signature on it, making it the law of the land.

This was not to be the last battle Dr. Emily fought for the rights of women. Her whole life could be said to have been that of a soldier on this particular front line. She joined with other men and women in an organization dedicated to wiping out the last traces of inequality between men and women, whether those inequalities were laws, or working conditions, or property rights, or job opportunities. People had helped her when she was a young woman; now she tried to help others.

But more and more she and Dr. Benjamin loosened their ties with their New York practices and hospitals and more and more they stayed in their charming house in New Canaan. "Little Meuse" it was called and that means in French—an escape. This was what it meant to both these people whose lives had been crowded and busy.

Next door her daughter and husband and family lived. Not far away was Dr. Henry Dunning and his wife Eleine, and their four sons and daughters: Henry Sage Dunning, Jr., Elaine, who had Americanized the French spelling of her mother's name, George Henry and Nancy Jefferson—and their children.

This meant a pleasant and happy—sometimes a noisy—

coming and going at the Barringers. So many young people constantly about kept them all young.

One day Dr. Henry and his wife arrived at Little Meuse and they were upset! They could hardly wait to greet Dr. Emily and Dr. Ben before they unloaded their problem. It was a big problem.

"A G.P. present!" Harry exploded. A G.P. present meant a grateful patient's present. "Delivered to the house while we were away and we knew nothing about it, or that it was coming, until we arrived home today. Do you know what it is? Great, enormous stone urns and birdbaths and a stone slab of a table for the garden!"

The humor of it struck his wife and she began to laugh. "You should see them. I don't know how it was possible for anything but the largest truck in the world and ten men to deliver them. Actually, they are quite nice but far more appropriate to the formal garden of a palace than to our garden."

Dr. Emily laughed, too, and Ben asked, with a twinkle in his gray eyes, "What are you going to do with them?"

"What can we do with them? Leave them there. They will be with us as long as we have the house—we couldn't possibly move them away. Oh, but it is funny!" Eleine said.

"Funny as a crutch," grumbled Dr. Henry, but in a second he was laughing, too, and then the talk turned to all the strange and wonderful and crazy gifts which grateful patients give to their doctors.

"I can remember one I *didn't* take and regretted bitterly not being able to take," said Emily. "When I was at Gouverneur we were never allowed to accept money from patients although a G.P. gift of anything else was permissible. One evening I had a hurry call to go to the Bowery Theater and Dick Bateman and I rushed over. As a matter of fact, it was he, not I, who earned that G.P. gift because when we came to the theater he suggested that we go around to the back door and not to the front. It was really thoughtful of him.

Well, we found one of those great, big, voluptuous, blond Bowery Theater stars had tripped during her dance and fallen and fractured her thigh. We went in through the back and I got splints on her and we took her out in a stretcher through the back. That was when the manager came to us with a gift for our tactfulness. If we had come in the front entrance—a doctor and ambulance driver—it would have caused a panic in the audience. So he handed us the gift—a derby hat crammed to the brim with dollar bills! How I hated to tell him we couldn't accept it! I was earning nothing and Dick Bateman's salary wasn't much, but the rules were strict on that subject. We left that theater feeling very self-righteous but very wistful over the emptiness of our pockets."

"But," she continued, "the G.P. present I shall never forget was my very first one at Gouverneur. I keep it among my treasures."

The young people who were listening thought of all of the beautiful and cherished things that their grandmother and great-aunt now owned, and wondered which one was this particular "treasure."

"It was during my first weeks at Gouverneur. A young man, really not yet a man but an adolescent, came into the dispensary with blood poisoning of his hand. He was afraid of losing it but I reassured him and he came back every day to have it treated. It was a painful process and I can say that the two of us suffered together during it."

Everyone knew that special quality of Dr. Emily: the way she would fight for a patient, pouring her energy and courage into him.

"The blood poisoning was cured," she went on. "He thanked me and I thought that was the last of him. But, no— the next day he was back again with a package so carefully wrapped, and with the proudest and the most bashful look on his face. He had gone to a lot of trouble to find just what he thought a lady would like. He had nobody to guide him in his selection—"

"But what was it?" one of her listeners cried impatiently.

She threw back her head and her infectious laughter startled them all. "It was a box with a glass top on it and a card which read: FOR THE LADY DOC—and in the box was the brightest, most frivolous, most gaudy yellow satin garters you ever saw, all ribbons and bows! How the staff, those four, did tease me about them . . . the rascals."

Time had mellowed the memory of the persecution and when she now thought of her four tormentors it was almost with affection . . . *those rascals.*

By 1948 Dr. Benjamin Barringer was not well enough to continue his practice and he retired. Dr. Emily was semiretired. Their home and their family occupied most of their thoughts. They remodeled the house, and Dr. Benjamin spent long hours happily painting in the garden.

In March of 1953, at the age of seventy-five, he died.

It was not unexpected. There was no great shock for Dr. Emily. Life could not ever be the same for her again, with the loss of the husband she had loved so dearly, but neither was she crushed by it. She went on as she had before. Although she no longer practiced medicine, she was still active working for equal rights for women; there were still her home and her children and grandchildren to console her.

The countryside of New Canaan is a particularly lovely spot in America. From her windows and her garden Dr. Emily could see the trees budding in the spring and coming to full greenness, changing to vivid colors in the autumn. There were sweet-scented flowers in the garden. Yet she would look at it and frequently her mind would return to another spot that she had loved—so different, so very different.

The East Side of New York. Steaming hot in summer and icy cold in winter—and how she had loved every bit of it! An ambulance call might take her to the tough streets or the busy streets or into a crowded, smelly, dark tenement house. It wasn't the dirt and the ugliness that she thought about so much, but the bravery of the people who lived in the East Side, who survived it and fought against it.

Naturally, her thoughts were frequently with the courageous women who had had to fight prejudice as well as everything else. Out of the slums of the East Side had come women who fought for better working conditions so that laws would finally be passed for only eight hours of work instead of ten or twelve; there would be good schools and protection for their children; the family would be kept together and the new generation would have its chance.

Out of the East Side had come teachers, writers, lawyers, skilled workmen, doctors—even geniuses of science and art.

She remembered so well one small tenement flat. She had visited it in the daytime and found it neat. The mother had stayed home that day to watch her sick child. That night Emily had to return, and she found the floor covered with sleeping people, wrapped up in blankets, and she had to step over them to reach her patient. The mother maintained her home, watched her child, worked during the day—and took in lodgers at night! With such incredible fortitude she earned the money for her family. Yet women were called the "weaker sex"!

Dr. Emily Dunning Barringer had seen many changes in her day. Women had broken through all kinds of barriers. Yet the fight was not entirely won. There was still prejudice. And the words of Dr. Jacobi came back to her again and again:

"Women must be willing to go up, to be knocked down again and again. . . ." They would, just as she had. Dr. Emily was sure and confident of the future and women's place in it. She had done her own part well.

On April 9, 1961, Dr. Emily Dunning Barringer died at the home of her son in New Milford, Connecticut.

INDEX

About the Author

IRIS NOBLE grew up on a ranch in the Crow's Nest Pass between Canada's Alberta and British Columbia. Her parents were American and when she was eleven they moved to Oregon. After graduating from the University of Oregon, she moved to Los Angeles and got her first job as a secretary at station KFI-KECA. She left there to work for Fawcett Publications and later was publicity director for a theatre-restaurant. After her marriage she came to New York City where she did freelance writing. In recent years she has made her home in San Francisco and has been devoting herself to writing both in the field of biography and teen-age fiction.